Cornish Ghosts and Legends

A. A Witch.   B   A Spirit raised by the Witch.
C. A Friar raising his Imps.   D A Fairy Ring.
E. A Witch rideing on the Devill through the Aire.
F. An Inchanted Castle.

Frontispiece to Richard Bovet's *Pandaemonium*, 1684 (British Library).

CORNISH GHOSTS AND LEGENDS

Compiled from William Bottrell's
*Traditions and Hearthside Stories
of West Cornwall*

Edited by J. A. Brooks

JARROLD

Acknowledgments

The publishers would like to thank the staff of the Local History Library at Redruth and the Curator and Librarian of the Royal Institution of Cornwall for their help in preparing this book. They have been particularly generous in allowing us to draw on their collection of engravings of Cornwall which, together with the illustrations from the original volumes and other contemporary engravings, embellish this book. The National Portrait Gallery and the British Library have also provided illustrations.

ISBN 0-8530-6960-3
© 1981 Jarrold Publishing
Published by Jarrold Publishing, Norwich
Printed in Great Britain 2/97

Contents

Preface

William Bottrell was a regular contributor to local periodicals long before the appearance of his first volume of *Traditions and Hearthside Stories of West Cornwall* in 1870. A second volume was published in 1880. Because all three books were published by subscription, the third volume repeats much material already used in the previous editions. At the time of its publication Bottrell was completely paralysed by the stroke that led to his death soon afterwards.

These stories are a wonderful monument to a man whose love of West Cornwall and its traditions made him painstakingly seek out and write down the dimly remembered legends of his forefathers. As he wrote in the Preface to the First Volume of stories:

> In a very few years these interesting traditions would have been lost, unless they had been preserved in some such form as the present volume is intended to supply; since modern customs, and the diffusion of the local news of the day, are superseding, in even the most remote districts, the semi-professional droll-tellers who were formerly welcomed at all firesides, fairs, and feasts for their recitals of the old ballads and stories in which they abounded, and of which their audience rarely tired.

Obviously nearly all the tales grow from the seed of a remarkable event about which the droll wove the story we read here. Bottrell's other rare gift was the light-heartedness with which he retold the tale. His tirades against the kill-joy clergy who attempted to stamp out the ancient customs and beliefs, and against the tyranny of domineering wives are as delightful as they are obviously heart-felt. However, many of the stories carry such a weight of digression that though they may be invaluable to the student they make difficult reading today. Thus some have been abridged and others omitted altogether. It is to Bottrell's eternal credit that the wit and vividness of his writing survives this treatment.

The author was born at Raftra in the parish of St Levan (within three miles of Land's End) on 7 March 1816. He was educated at Penzance Grammar School and at Bodmin before spending some time in France after 1837. He returned to help his father with the family farm for some years before becoming English master in the Seminary of Quebec between 1847 and 1851. Subsequently he returned to live in Penzance (at No. 4 Clare Street) and, in later life, in a picturesquely situated cliffside cottage on Hawkes Point, Carbis Bay. He died at Dove Street, St Ives, on 27 August 1881.

Some Cornish Ghosts

The Ghost of Stythians

(The story is true in its main incidents, though the names, for obvious reasons, are fictitious.)

bout twenty years ago, there lived in the parish of Stythians a very hard-working and careful old widow, called An Jenny Hendy. The penurious habits of the old woman seemed very unreasonable, because she had no children nor other relations who had any claims on her. An Jenny's savings must have been considerable, as she had long owned a comfortable cottage and several acres of rich land, with gardens and orchards, all in good order and cultivated by herself with but little assistance from anyone. Though the old creature had no near relations, there were scores about, all over that part of the country, who claimed cousinship, and who were most eager to please the mistress of such nice cows, pigs and poultry, to say nothing of house, land and other gear. These good folks became particularly attentive to Cousin Jenny when there appeared to be the least hopes of her having a speedy release from the cares and griefs of this world, and they showed much more anxiety about preparing the dame for her heavenward journey than she relished, particularly when reminded that she ought, as she had one foot in the grave, to prepare for her latter end by giving to some good cause of which the lecturer was an unworthy member, and so on.

In general, An Jenny told the pious

11

beggars, in no measured terms, that if one foot was in the grave she would take all the care possible to keep the other out of it, as long as she could; and that, when she wanted her duds no longer, she would leave them to some honest body – if she could find one who worked, and did not talk for a living; so they might go and groan, turn up the whites of their eyes, spread out their fingers in sanctified style somewhere else, for anything they would get of her.

At last the old woman showed more regard for a young fellow of the same family name who lived in service with a farmer near by. When the young man had finished his day's work and had a few hours to spare, he would lend a hand and do any odd job for An Jenny, to keep her place in good order, without thinking or pretending to any claims of kindred, though he was as near a relation as she knew of. He left his wages with her for safe keeping, and An Jenny often said to others that she would add something to his nest-egg, if he took home a decent maid for a wife. But, long before Robin thought in earnest of giving up the happy estate of a single life and a sweetheart, he came over one Saturday night to deposit his wages with the old dame, and found her seated in her chair dead and cold. He called in the nearest neighbour, and they discovered, from the cows not having been milked in the morning, and other regular dairy work left undone, that she must have died the previous night.

When Robin, with the assistance of a neighbour's wife, had the body laid out and all put in order, they took from the old woman's pocket the key of her chest, and opened it, making sure that in the skibbet they would find some hundreds of pounds at least; but after searching chest, drawers, cupboards, the thatch, and every likely and unlikely hole and corner where the old woman might have secreted the young man's savings and her own, not a penny was to be found. Some of the cousins had visited the dame a few days before she died, though none of them came to the burying, the expense of which was defrayed by Robin out of his wages.

As might be expected, there was much guessing, enquiry, and surmise about what could have become of the money. Cousins, one and all, declared that they had no hand in the pie. The young man was much put out thus to lose the hard-earned savings of many years, besides the hopes of what An Jenny had promised to lay in the nest of her own rusty guineas. He took possession, as many were found who had heard the old woman declare that whatever she had to leave she would give to Robin; and none of the cousins had so good a right, on the score of kindred. Besides, the dame had made a will, bequeathing all the property to him. This will was not to be found; still as the witnesses to this document were all living, everybody considered that Robin had good right to take what he found.

After many more vain searches, all the neighbours agreed that the only way to get any knowledge of what had become of the money was to consult Tammy, the white witch of Helston. Now as Robin, as well as most others in the west, had heard of and believed in the extraordinary powers of this wise woman, he had no doubt of what everybody had told him, that she could raise the spirit of An Jenny Hendy and get her to say what was become of the cash; or rather, as they said, to tell him who of all the cousins had laid hands on it.

Robin, having made up his mind to consult the white witch, went to her abode one Saturday evening, about a month after the old woman's death. Tammy agreed that she could see no other way of clearing up the mystery than to raise the old woman's spirit, and get it to speak to him. 'But you must know,' said the witch, 'that it is a dreadful thing to undertake, and I shall want some money – two pounds at least – that we may get herbs, drugs, and other things not easily procured, for the sake of securing myself and you against any evil influences of the spirit, and that we may either put her to rest or send her to torment those who have stolen the money. If you can give me a pound now, to get what we want, I'll have all ready to rise the spirit some night next week, if you will.'

The man, well knowing that this precious white witch did nothing without forehand pay, gave her a sovereign, and promised to meet her, with a horse, on the road to Stythians churchyard, the next Thursday night, by eleven, so that they might be at the old woman's grave before midnight.

Thursday night came. Robin procured a quiet horse, stuffed a bag with straw, to serve as a pillion, secured it on behind the pad, and rode away, soon after dark, to meet the witch. Within two miles, or so, of the churchyard where the old woman lay, Robin met the witch, who wasn't at all pleased because she had to walk so far. A drink from the bottle of brandy which he carried to help quell his fears soon calmed her temper, however. For some time after Tammy mounted, they spoke but little; she kept mumbling something to herself in what seemed a strange lingo to the man. When he asked what she was palavering of, the witch replied, 'You must keep silence, while I am communing with the spirits that attend me. I send them to prepare the one I am about to raise. It's well they're not visible to you, because the sight of them is more than ordinary flesh and blood, such as yours, can stand. Now you arn't afraid, are 'e?' says she, grasping him by the arm.

When they arrived in Stythians' churchtown it was near midnight. No lights were to be seen in the houses. After securing the horse in some place, Tammy stalked away towards the churchyard, all the time mumbling something to herself, and only paused when they came to the churchyard stile. Then, turning round to Robin, she said, 'Oh! I'm nearly out of breath, with orderan the obstinate sperats about, and there's one now in this churchyard, more troublesome than all the rest, that I must subdue, or it may overcome me some night, when the least expected. I must have a pull at the bottle before I begin what is harder and more dangerous work still.'

After taking a good drink of the brandy, she said, 'Don't you be frightened even if you happen to see Old Nick. Perhaps it would be well to tie a handkerchief over your eyes because the Devil will often be here trying to catch the sperats, and the sight of his saucer eyes of fire, ugly horns and cloven hoof, is enough to frighten one into fits. And oh! the smell of brimstone he brings along with him es enough to poison one! You arn't afraid, are 'e, that you're trembling so?'

'No,' groaned the man, 'I don't mind brimstone, nor the old gentleman either, much; perhaps, after all, he esn't half so bad as he's made out to be.'

'Well,' said the witch, when they came close to the churchyard gate, 'you know the Old One can't pass the stile and put his hoof on consecrated ground; that's the way he and his hounds are mostly keepan watch at the gates, or beatan round some place near. Now that's the reason why the poor sperats can't venture to go over the churchyard wall, where I have often seen them perched as close together as they could stick, grinning at Old Nick, and his hounds without heads, for if they lean over the least bit they are picked off on his horns and away they go – you know where, don't 'e? But don't you be frightened, lad. The churchyard is crowded with thousands of sperats,' she continued; 'think of all who have been buried there for hundreds of years. Ef you would like to see them I'll touch your eyes with a bit of salve from the corners of mine; then you will behold them as I do now. There,' said she, pointing with her staff towards the old weatherbeaten church, 'all the roof is covered with them, watching for the bit of glimmering moon now glistening on the tower, and there! – see them pushing each other over the top and fighting for a perch on the pinnacles that they may get a view of the place they once inhabited.'

'Hush, do, An Tammy; don't 'e go on so,' said Robin.

'Why you needn't fear them,' she replied, 'these old ghosts are mere worn-out shadows, whose bodies, many of them, were buried here long before this church was built. I like to look at them. Perhaps you can see a gleam of light showing through the windows on the eastern side of the porch! That's from the spirits inside, acting over again their christens, weddings and funerals. Many of them prefer such grim shows as the last, and pass most of their time burying each other over and over for the thousandth time, in all the various modes that quick or dead can devise. I wish you could see those perched over on the eastern end, where the moonlight is just beginning to glimmer. They are the grand ones whose dust was laid inside the church! They look very proud still, especially the women decked out in all their ruffs, trains, furbelows and old steeple-crowns. There they march, on the ridge of the roof, in grand state. Those among them dressed in shrouds, are younger ghosts, who lived when these ugly things came into fashion. But the old gentlemen in their cocked hats, square coats and riding boots, look very grim and melancholy, especially when they hear the hue and cry of the wish hounds! Don't they almost wish then to be in the black huntsman's place for a change. Oh! I hear them now,' said the witch, making a start and grasping Robin's arm; 'Come into the churchyard – we have no time to spare. You are prepared now, I hope, to see An Jenny Hendy's ghost riding slowly from the grave in shroud or sheet – her face appearing the same as it now looks in her coffin. And mind, you must speak to the spirit when it comes close to ye, as I am now, or it may do ye much harm! Now, are you ready?' said she, at the same time striking with her staff on the gate till it flew open.

Robin was so fear-struck that the hair stood on end on his head. A cold sweat poured over him like rain. He could neither move nor speak for some minutes. At last he gasped out, 'Do tell me, An Tammy, can 'e put her away again as soon as I know what's become of the money?'

'You must risk that,' Tammy replied, 'we have now no more time for talking. You and everybody else know how Janny Tregeagle tormented the one who raised him on a like occasion. All depends on the temper she may be in, and the leave she gets! Why, she may jump on the horse and ride home behind thee for what one can tell before she is risen. It will soon be too late. Come along, and stand at the foot of the grave that you may face her when she rises.'

The witch then entered the churchyard. As she passed the gate, most unearthly howls and yells, with a noise which Robin took to be the tramp of Old Nick's steeds, was heard, at no great distance, getting louder and louder until it seemed to be near the burying-ground.

'Do 'e come back, An Tammy,' gasped the man, as he seized hold of her cloak; 'I believe I can't go any further tonight; and as you have got the sovereign you can keep en.'

'What! you white-livered fool,' says she, turning round and grasping Robin with her long bony fingers; 'come in, speak to the sperat, know where thy money es, and get it back again like a man, to be sure! Rise the sperat or leave et alone, dusen't thee think that I'll tramp such a journey as this for nothing more than I was paid the other night. Turn out another pound, or I'll summon the spirit hither! If she once gets out of the churchyard she will haunt thee thy life long – perhaps make thee shorten thy days to get rid of the torment; walking or riding, sleeping or waking, she shall be with thee!'

The infernal clatter of hell-hounds and hoofs seemed still approaching, when Robin said,

'Here, take the money,' handing the witch another pound; 'les be off from this wisht place; come home with me, do, and stay till day.'

'As you like,' Tammy replied, in pocketing the cash. Then, in moving away from the churchyard, she gave another unearthly yell. 'That's a signal to one of my sperats that we shan't want him anymore tonight,' said she. Robin unfastened his horse from the furze-rick, and the beast carried them both back to what had lately been An Jenny Hendy's abode.

A few hours brought daylight. After partaking of a substantial breakfast, the witch said that she ought to have more pay for her night's work. Robin, however, refused to comply with her request; and, on leaving, she said, 'I don't know but what An Jenny's sperat was so much disturbed with our last night's work, that it may cause her to come back, if she esn't here already, which I rather fear may be the case. If she disturbs 'e much you can send for me, and I'll do my best to put her quiet again.' Saying this, she took her departure.

The day was a troubled one for poor Robin. At every turn he thought he caught glimpses of An Jenny, or heard her rattling the milk-pans as she was used to when doing odd jobs in the dairy. At last, fearing to remain alone in the house any longer, he went down to hoe potatoes in a field near the town-place. He was hard at work when he felt that feeling in the spine that comes of being watched, and from the corner of the eye he saw a figure that seemed, when observed in this manner, to bear an amazing resemblance to that of the dead old lady. What relief he felt when this apparition spoke out to him in manly tones!

'What cheer, cousin Robin? Am I altered so much since I've been away that thee dussen't know me, then? Why art thee staring at me so, like a fool frightened? Come here, and shake a paw with they old comrade. I left my ship in Falmouth harbour early this morning to pass a few weeks ashore, enquired the news about old friends as I came along, and found out that thee wert here in the old woman's shoes; and how dos't a get on, mate?'

'Oh! the Devil take my stupid head, and the old 'oman too,' says Robin, when he saw that what he had taken for An Jenny's apparition was no other than an old comrade, who had been away to sea some years; 'west thee believe it, cousin Jack, that, with all the time thinken about the old woman I took thee for her sperat. I can't tell how glad I am to see thee after so long a time, not knowing if thee wert alive or dead. Let's go in; we'll soon have something cooked for dinner.'

When a drink of good rum had put a little more heart into Robin he related what took place between him and the white witch over night, saying, in addition, that he wouldn't pass such a time again for twice the old woman's brass. The tar replied that he believed all the ghosts he saw were conjured up by his fears and fancies, aided by the witch's ranting and other tricks of her trade – he'd known her of old.

When they had finished dinner, the sailor, after hearing more about the dreadful apparitions, said, 'Mate, if I hadn't known thee from thee cradle, I should say thee wert as d—d a coward and fool as es to be found between the Land's End and London churchtown; for I can see, plain as a handspike, that the goings on of old Tammy was intended to frighten thee. She rise a spirit! the d—d witch, no, no more than I can. Let's go into Helston, this afternoon, and ask her if a substitute will do? I'm a fourth or fifth cousin, as well as you, to the old dear that's dead, Lord rest her; so I might ask her very well what she may have done with her shiners!'

The young men arrived in Helston about nightfall. They went immediately to a doctor, and Robin was bled, from a very common notion that blood-letting is useful to counteract the bad effects of a fright. Then, after partaking of a good supper and plenty of grog, Robin entered Tammy's dwelling, and his companion remained outside.

Tammy was only persuaded to accept Jack as a substitute after all her objections had been demolished by argument and the promise of even more payment given. Finally the sailor was called in. He pretended to believe all the witch told them, appearing to her as green as grass and as innocent as a new-born babe. He gave her a sovereign, promised her more if the job was ended to their satisfaction, and agreed to meet her on the road with a horse the following night.

Next evening, the tar met Tammy. After treating her to a good dram, they jogged along several miles, talking about the wonders she had performed in her time. For the most part Jack kept silent, and observed all her manoeuvres, till they came to the churchyard gate. Then, pretending to be rather scared by the yelling, howling, tramping, and clatter of hoofs, which seemed to be near them, he said, 'An Tammy, es that terrible noise we hear made by the old gentleman and his hounds sure enough?'

'Of that you may be certain,' she replied, 'yet I do hope that you will be able to stand all you will see, and not get any harm from the sight, as there's no doctor at hand to bleed 'e. You ought to have been provided with a quart or two of cold water, because, in case of a fright, drinking that es the next best thing to bleeding to keep your hair from turning grey.'

'Now cease thy palaver,' says the tar, 'I'm come here to see and speak with the old woman's ghost and don't care a d— if thee do'st raise all the spirits in the churchyard; I'll face them, never fear; so set about it as soon as thou wilt.'

Without further parley the witch led the way into the churchyard. Then the infernal noise ceased. All became as still as the dead. They turned off the path leading to the church door, passed between tombstones and over graves, until they came to a clearer space near a large, high headstone. Here the witch stopped and said, in solemn tones, 'I will not take you close alongside her grave, because it is even more than my strength, used as I am to such things, can well endure, to behold the ghastly apparition, with shrouded head, rising from the ground. No, I will summon the spirit hither, that it may get away from the grave before you see it.'

She then marked out a circle by drawing her staff on the ground

18

three times round the man, at the same time mumbling in her unknown tongue. This done, turning to the sailor, she said, 'Now mind, for your life, that you don't move out of this charmed ring which I have made to protect thee, and if you are still determined I will now begin and summon the spirit.'

The witch, holding out her staff towards the spot where the old woman was buried, began her incantation with long strange words, slowly pronounced. Then she continued in a louder tone, 'Spirit of Jane Hendy, in the name of all the powers above and below, I summon thee to arise from the grave and appear before me and this man! By the spirits of fire, air, earth and water, I summon thee to arise! Come hither, appear, and speak to this man! Come!' This she said three times, rising her voice at each repetition until it ended in a shriek.

The witch paused. All was silent for a moment, and then were heard, most fearful, because unusual, sounds, which more than any other earthly noise resembled the crashing or rending of wood and stones, mingled with painful moans, groans and shrieks, which seemed to come from the old woman's grave. The witch, stretching out her arms, her red cloak and grey hair streaming back on the wind, pointed with her staff towards the place whence these frightful sounds proceeded, and said, 'Behold, it cometh: be thou prepared!'

Then the sailor saw by the glimmering light of a waning moon a tall ghastly figure rising from amid the tombstones, a hundred feet or so from where he stood. This hideous form, in winding-sheet and shroud, stalked towards them with measured step and slow, so near that the sailor saw its grisly locks and glaring eyes. A moment more and he sees its ashy-pale face within a yard of him. The man's hair bristled up on his head, and, in spite of his disbelief in ghosts, he shrunk back out of the circle, towards the witch, who cowered and fell down seemingly terror-stricken, behind a large headstone, within arm's length of the sailor, when, in terror, he had scarcely the power to exclaim, 'In the name of God who or what art thou?'

The ghost, in a hollow voice, replied, 'Wherefore dost thou disturb my rest in the grave. The wise woman should have given thee other counsel. What art thou to me? For this deed of darkness I will mark both thee and her this night, and haunt thee all the days of thy miserable life. Devil take me ef I don't.'

Saying this the ghost stretched forth its arms from under the shroud, and, with a strong hand, grasped the sailor, who gave it a blow with his fist and laid it sprawling on the sod. Indeed he no longer

feared this apparition when he heard the familiar termination of its long speech. Besides, instead of bringing with it the infernal sulphurous air proper to a ghost, the breath of this one smelt strongly of tobacco and gin, and it hiccoughed and sneezed in a way very unbecoming a spirit.

The sailor had no sooner settled the ghost than he was all but knocked down by a stunning blow from the witch, who, a moment before, apparently terror-stricken, shrunk cowering in the rear. Recovering himself he wrenched the stick from her hands; then, turning to the apparition, he saw it on its legs again, but (divested of shroud and sheet) in the form of Jemmy T—, old Tammy's good man, who was well known to the sailor and to everybody else in that part of the country.

The sailor was so indignant at the attempted deception that he continued to thrash the former ghost most unmercifully until Jemmy begged for quarter and promised to hand back the money Robin had paid them. Tammy came forward with the cash in her hand and said, 'Dussen'a kill the poor ghost.'

Jack gave over the well-merited beating, pocketed the sovereigns, sat down on the tomb, and said, 'To give the Devil his due, thee art a far better white witch than thy man is a ghost.' Turning to Jemmy, who was now on his forkle-end, he asked. 'What contrivance hast a to make such an infernal noise?'

'Why, nothing more,' Jemmy replied, 'than my own voice, an old tin pan, and a stick to beat on the tombstone or rattle on the church door, as best suited the purpose. What Robin took for the tramp of Old Nick's steed, and the cry of his pack, was only the music of my making.'

The witch then coming forward and addressing the sailor said, 'Now listen to me. I have been thinking of a plan, and ef thy wit, Jack, es equal to thy courage, this sperat-risan may be turned for some account to Robin, after all. The story es gone round far and near that he was going to employ me and that An Jenny was to be called up; but few doubt my power to do it; so let's give out now that she has appeared, and declared to us who have taken the money, and, farther, that unless the stolen money and other things that belonged to her are brought to her late abode within a month, her sperat will haunt them, and the white witch shall mark them so that all the world may know them by one blind eye; and anything more may be said, that can be thought of as likely to frighten the cousins into doing what we wish.'

Jack replied, 'There is something in that plan. Robin and I will think over et.' Then, leaving the witch and her mate in the churchyard to gather up their ghostly trappings and infernal machinery, he went to rejoin his comrade whom he expected to find in the public-house; but Robin, fearing some harm might happen to the sailor, so far overcame his dread of ghosts, and the old gentleman with his headless hounds, as to venture out and on the road, within a stone's throw of the churchyard. Here he stood, quaking with fear, when the sailor came up and said, 'Cheer up comrade, for I've seen and spoken with the ghost; we shall soon know what's become of the money, and get et back again or it's much to me.'

He then explained how the old woman's ghost was personated by Tammy's drunken husband, and how the sounds which he, confused with fear, took for the hell-hounds' cry, and the tramp of the Devil's hunter, were all produced by the precious scoundrel who acted the ghost with very simple contrivances. He then told Robin what the witch proposed, and asked him what he thought of the plan.

'Well,' Robin replied, 'there's no harm to try.'

Our youngsters, still seeing light in the public-house, entered, and found that all the inmates had long gone to bed, except the landlady, and she, thinking that something unusual was going on, wanted to find out what kept the young men abroad so late. After tantalising the fat dame with a show of reluctance on their part to say anything about An Jenny or her money, the sailor told her that the spirit had been raised, spoke of the ghostly communication, and hinted that it might be well for those who took the old woman's money, or who owed her anything, if they would make all right with his mate; otherwise, they would be marked and haunted.

'Good Lord! wonders will never cease!' exclaimed the dame of the inn; 'and I'm glad that you have told me, because there was a trifle between An Jenny and me for some eggs. It had slipped my memory, and I've forgotten what it was exactly, but you can settle it with the liquor and take a few pints more to make sure that all is right.'

Before many days passed, the story about the old woman's ghost having been raised was carried by the gossips all over the neighbourhood; and those who had taken her money, as well as others who had any dealings with her, were so terrified for fear of a visit from 'the sperat' that in less than a month papers containing considerable sums, and others with only a few pence, were thrown through the window-bars into the dairy. Some, like the landlady, openly settled their accounts, and many to whom the departed owed a trifle, if only a halfpenny (the worst of all ghostly debts), begged Robin, or the witch, to tell the spirit that her debt was forgiven.

An Jenny's ghost, dressed in her red cloak and little old black bonnet, was often seen in by-lanes, on lonely moors and downs, both by night and at noonday. No one could tell why she wandered in such out-of-the-way places, and vanished as suddenly as she appeared. Yet the main purpose was served because, when it became known that she was in a walking state, those who owed her anything hastened to settle their accounts with her heir.

One night a violent gale stripped the thatch from a great part of Robin's dwelling, laying bear the punion-end; and there, pushed far into a hole which had been covered by the thatch, he found the old woman's pocket, and in this a roll of papers, among which were notes of some value and the old dame's will.

During the two or three months that Jack remained ashore he mostly lived with Robin, or at least stayed with him overnight. Then, they neither saw nor heard anything to scare them; but the tar was no sooner gone to sea, than Robin heard the spirit going about in the house, putting things to rights, all night long. As he could get little sleep, from one disturbance and another, and disliking to live without some companion in flesh and blood in the haunted place, he soon brought home a wife. Then An Jenny Hendy's ghost took her departure, and Robin enjoyed sound rest at last.

The Ghost Layer

We do not know if An Jenny Hendy's ghost went to rest of its own free will, or whether any divine assisted in binding the troubled spirit to the grave. There need, however, be no difficulty about getting a ghost laid.

We have just heard of a local preacher, living in the district between Camborne and Helston, who, according to his own account, has put many troublesome spirits to rest, generally by settling for them their mundane affairs, about which they were troubled, by reasoning with and advising them to stay below, bear their punishment with a good heart, and hope for better times. He allowed that sometimes he was merely deluding the ghosts; yet, no matter, the end sought was attained! As he had a rather uncommon adventure in laying one ghost we give his (abridged) account of the enterprise.

From some trifling cause the spirit got back again to its late abode before the mourners had quitted the public-house in churchtown, where, as is customary, they stopped a while to treat and take leave of their friends, who had come to the funeral from a distance.

The ghost became, at once, so annoying, that none could rest in the house with it, and, a few nights after the burial, the family of the deceased, not knowing what to do to obtain any quiet, fetched the preacher, who was believed to possess extraordinary knowledge of spiritual matters and power over the ghostly world and its inhabitants. He entered the haunted house alone. After many hours passed in prayer and expostulation with the obstinate spirit, it at last consented to return to its grave and stay there, if the exorcist and preacher would accompany it to the churchyard, to see it safely landed there.

And now happened the most remarkable part of the affair. About midnight the ghost layer bound the spirit with a piece of new rope and fastened the other end of it round his own waist, that the spirit mightn't give him the slip. The latter, gentle as a lamb, was then led out of the house; but it had no sooner crossed the doorsill than the dwelling was surrounded by a pack of yelping hounds, of which the town-place was full, and the Old One riding up the lane in a blaze of fire.

The spirit, to save itself from being caught by the hounds and huntsman, mounted high up in the air, taking the man (hanging by the middle) with it. Away they went, over trees, hills and water. In less than a minute they passed over some miles, and alighted in the churchyard, close by the spirit's grave, which the man saw open, blue sulphurous flames issuing therefrom, and he heard, coming from below, most horrid shieks and moans.

The ghost, knowing it was no use contending with the man of faith, only stopped to say farewell and then descended into its grave, which immediately closed. The man – overcome by being borne with lightning speed through the air or by the infernal fumes rising from the open grave – fell down in a fit, from which he did not recover till daybreak, and then he was scarcely able to leave the churchyard. When near the town-place, which he had left with the spirit, in the branch of a tree he found his hat, that must have fallen from his head on first mounting through the air.

The most probable solution of this story (told in good faith and firmly believed) is that the ghost layer, after taking too much spirit in the public-house, rambled into the churchyard, there fell asleep, and dreamed the rest.

The Demon-Mason of Lamorna

The meaning of the melodious name of Lamorna, in which one hears the murmur of the waves, has been, and is still, a mystery to Cornish scholars. It may be that it is formed out of the words *Lan-mor-nan* which would signify enclosed vale by the sea. A short way up the valley from the cove, and on its eastern side, is Bosava. Few more pleasing scenes for a rural picture can be found than the bowery lane, brook and mill here; and the high hills crowned with hoar rocks in the background form such a combination of savage and sylvan beauty as most artists delight in. The common saying of the inhabitants of this neighbourhood that 'Bosava was the first house built after the flood', implies that they regard it as the most ancient habitation of the vale.

Little more than a century ago there might be seen, just below Bosava mill, the ruins of a very old house, which must have been much larger than any other dwelling in the glen, and of superior masonry to anything seen elsewhere except in the old churches. In accordance with the usual habit of simple primitive folks to assign a supernatural agent (whether giant, saint or demon) as the cause of every extraordinary performance, and to connect the agency with the religion or mythology of the time and place, the erection of this remarkable dwelling was ascribed to a demon-mason, who engaged to build a house of better workmanship than was ever seen in the parish before, for an old miserly cobbler named Lenine, on the usual conditions – that the employer was to depart with the demon craftsman at a stated time and serve him. They say that one of the boots which old Lenine made for the dark gentleman-mason was much larger than the other, to hide his cloven foot. No one, at first, except the old cobbler, knew whence the dark and silent workman came, nor was it known how or when he departed: yet, in an incredibly short space of time, the building was completed, all the walling done in the old-fashioned style of rubble-work (now lost) of placing the loosing edges of the stones and the pinners all on the outside, so that the rain never penetrated the walls.

This mason, or devil, seldom used compass or square, plumb-line or level; yet his work was as true, and the walls were as even, as if he had intended to build him a tower. On a boldly projecting stone was displayed the figure of the mason's head, with long oval face, high forehead, and straight features. From among the ivy which soon overgrew the gable, this strange face, perched up on high, seemed to look down on all who passed by. The windows were all on the sunny side and ends of the house; but he made the door, according to the custom, common enough in old times, on the north side; and not a bad plan either, as one may, nine rainy days out of ten, leave the door open when to the north. In the gable, over the arched doorway of the porch, the mason placed a fine-grained diamond-shaped stone, on which he cut the exact features of the grinning, griping old miser, and surrounded the grim visage with a garland, or frame, of broken oak-branches, with leaves and acorns, all as finely cut in stone as if they had been carved in oak. Yet the chimney-stacks were the crowning glory of the building – they were of ashlar work and much higher than any seen here before: about a quarter of their height from the top, they were surrounded by a bold moulding; above this they were contracted to their summits in a beautifully carved outline.

We do not know much about the inside of Lenine's house. They say that the hall (we didn't call the best room in any such house a parlour then) served the old miser for a cobbler's shop, and as a mere lumber-room for the wreck of such fine things as belonged to his family in old days, when they had been grand folks: and the old cobbler had his full share of family pride, if but little besides. Over the great fireplace of the hall was more stone-carving, that the old miser said was the Lenine's or Lanyon's coat of arms; an old rusty sword was hung over this.

The strange mason from the other world had spared no pains, and took such pride in his work, that he thought nothing of trudging away down to Lamorna cliff to pick out the stone he wanted for a particular piece of work, and of carrying the same (often a load enough for a horse) home on his shoulder. A rule he never wanted. He could see at a glance the stone to fit the place, and the great stones – rocks one may call them – which he hoisted with a tackle of his own invention, for the corners and window-jambs, were set to a hair. Much more one might say about the fine work that the mason would be at from the first dawn of the long summer's day till dark night: ceaselessly, and in silence, he was for ever working away, while the old man and his boy tempered the clay or mixed the mortar. Between the three the timbers were placed for the roof and the house thatched: then the builder departed, no one knew how, nor exactly when.

Old Lenine enjoyed the house in his dismal way for many years after it had been finished, in all respects according to contract, by the honest mason-devil. The term was drawing near to a close for which it had been agreed that old Lenine was to live in his grand mansion, before he had to pay the builder; yet he did not seem to think much about it, and hammered away at his lapstone as if he did not care a cobbler's cuss for what was soon to come.

At last the term expired, and the cloven-footed craftsman returned to claim his own. The night he arrived (late as it was when he reached Bosava) he found old Lenine mending a pair of shoes for some neighbour. The cobbler desired his visitor, who was for immediate departure, to let him finish the job and the inch of candle remaining. The good-natured simple devil consented; then, when he turned his back a moment and went out to see how his work stood the beating of wind and weather, that instant the old cobbler blew out the candle and placed it in the Bible. The devil, as one may expect, was much enraged to find himself fooled by the old miser, and declared from that

time old Lenine should never be able to keep a whole roof on the house nor anybody else after him, so that he would find himself worse off than if he would go then, like a man to his word. The old cobbler cursed and swore that, roof or no roof, he would remain in his house, in spite of all the black gentry in the place the dark workman came from, as long as one stone stood on another. The crow of the cock soon after made the devil decamp, and, in taking his departure, he raised a whirlwind which blew off all the thatch from one side of the roof.

Old Lenine tried every means that he, or anyone else could ever think of, to keep a sound roof over his head, but all in vain. By the time he had taken his thatching tools off the roof of his high house (where the ladder was always left), a black cloud would be seen to gather up far out at sea: soon after, the wind would be roaring, shrieking and moaning to beat and blow around the cobbler's house until scarcely as much thatch would be left on the rafters as would make a goose nest. Yet the old miser did not care, for in spite of wind and weather he stuck to his castle all the time he lived and as long as the stones were left together. His death only took place many years after the building of his dwelling, and there was not much left of him to die, as his old carcase had gone to next to nothing. Whether he died in a natural way no one could say for certain. Those who inherited the property thought they would keep a roof on such a fine high house, that they might live in it, or let it, but they were mistaken, because the contest between the cobbler and the devil was going on with more obstinacy than ever. Old Lenine might be heard every night making the walls resound with the noise of his hammer ringing on the lapstone: even by day he would often be heard beating his leather. If stones were placed on the roof to help to secure the thatch it was not safe to come within a long distance of the place, as the stones would be thrown about by invisible hands, and hurled with such force from the roof to the road that many persons, in coming and going to the mill, got badly hurt; at last, when it was found that no one could live in Lenine's house, and few (on account of the strange doings there) cared to come near Bosava mill, the miller sent for Parson Corker, who was noted for having strange intercourse with the invisible world; or rather, the primitive people of the west believed him to possess the supernatural powers required to exorcise the evil one, to drive the night wanderer back into his grave, and so bind the poor ghost that he would never get loose again.

The parson was also such a noted sportsman that he was rarely seen except on horseback. He always came into church booted and spurred, to be ready for the chase as soon as he passed the churchyard gate and found his man and horse waiting for him at the cross. He so delighted in the sports of wood and field that, with the earliest dawn of the dewy morn, the hills around echoed the cry of his hounds and rang with the blast of his bugle-horn. The reverend huntsman, ghost layer, and devil-driver being a bachelor, lived with his cousins, the Trezillians, in Trezidder; and that he might enjoy the more liberty with his boon companions (as some thought, for practising the magic arts), he had a kind of retreat, summer-house, or prospect-place called the Plaisance built like a tower of two rooms, with fireplaces, etc., erected on the brow of the hill in Trezidder downs, where it overlooked the valley of Penberth and the highroad over Buryan hill. The parson's retreat was comfortably furnished, the upper storey as a bedroom; under the window-seats and all around the walls of both rooms were cupboards and lockers as in a ship's cabin. Here he would often pass many days and nights shut up alone, or only with someone of the same eccentric tastes as himself; and here one night the miller found the parson, after a day's hunt, holding a revel-rout among his companions of the chase.

The miller begged the parson to come to Bosava without delay, and to exert his power on the devil and cobbler. He thought that if the parson could not succeed in driving them away, he might at least, as he was a justice, bind them over to keep the peace.

After the parson and his friends had well fortified themselves, as well as the miller, with plenty of strong drink (that they might be the better able to undertake the difficult work), they all started about midnight from the parson's Plaisance for the scene of their ghostly operations, and arrived at Bosava in the small hours of the morning.

They say that when the parson, assisted by Dr Maddern and the miller, drew the magic pentagram and sacred triangle, within which they placed themselves for safety, and commenced the other ceremonies, only known to the learned, which are required for the effectual subjugation of restless spirits, an awful gale sprung up in the cove and raged up the vale with increasing fury, until scarcely a tree was left standing in the bottom. Yet there was hardly a breath of wind stirring in other places. The parson, undaunted, read on and performed more powerful operations in the art of exorcism, till the sweat boiled from his body so that there was not a dry thread on him. He was beginning to fear that he had met with more than his match, when the whole force of the storm gathered itself around the haunted house, and the tree to which the parson had been clinging, that he might not be blown away, was rooted from the ground and swept by the gale across the water. Then the thatch, timbers and stones were seen, by the lightning flashes, to fly all over the bottom of the valley. One of the sharp spars from the thatch stuck in the parson's side, and made a wound that pained him ever after. Yet, not to be baffled, the parson made the black spirit hear spells that were stronger still. A moment later the devil (as if in defiance) had made a clean sweep of the roof: from amid the wreck of the building a figure was seen to rise in the shape of the dark master-mason and fly away in the black thunder-cloud, with his level, square, plumb-line, compasses and other tools around him.

After the devil had disappeared there was a lull in the tempest. The brave parson then tried his power on the cobbler, who might still be heard beating his lapstone harder than ever. The Reverend Mr Corker, after summoning old Lenine to appear, and after much trouble in chasing the obstinate spirit of the old miser from place to place, at last caught him in the pulrose under the mill-wheel. Then the ghost threw his hammer and lapstone at the parson's head; at the same time he cried out, 'Now, Corker, that thee art come I must be gone, but it's only for a time.' Luckily the parson was too well acquainted with spiritual weapons to let ghostly tools do him any harm. The night was passed. The parson's power had compelled the demon and cobbler to depart. After making a wreck of the house between them, the parson could do no more for the miller. But a few days after it was found that the old cobbler had returned to the charge, making more noise and annoyance about the place than ever, by broad daylight even as bad as by night, and that the parson could only hunt him from spot to spot about the wreck of the haunted place, without being able to make the noises cease from amid the ruins. It was then decided to demolish all the walls of the devil's building.

Thus the best piece of work ever seen in this part of the country was long ago destroyed, and the stones employed for building hedges and outhouses. No one cared to use them about any dwelling-house, for fear that the old miserly cobbler might claim them and again settle down to beat his lapstone beside them.

The Haunted Chamber of Trewoof

A quarter of an hour's walk brings us from Bosava to the gateway where the Lamorna road joins the highway to the Land's End. Here, the pleasant woody glen expands itself into a broad bottom, surrounded by green hills. On a woody knoll, gently rising in the midst, are situated the remains of the old mansion-house of Trewoof (more commonly called Trove).*

The great house used to have a noted haunted chamber in the outer end of the gable, over the brewhouse, which, with the malt-rooms over, took up nearly all the wing on the southern side of the kitchen-court. High up in the gable, alongside an ivy-covered chimney-stack, a little window might be discovered among the branching ivy at the time the sun was sunk so low as to glisten on the few diamond-shaped panes left in the casement. Yet no one could ever find any room within to which this window belonged. The door of the room or closet, with the mysterious window, was probably walled up because that old part of the house was always disturbed at night with the humming of a spinning-wheel and other noises usually made when carding wool or spinning the yarn.

A story about the little glimmering look-out among the ivy-bushes, where the owls had always nested, and through which a light would often be seen to flash and fade away of a winter's night, says that it opened into a garret haunted by some ancient housekeeper of Trove who had once been young and fair; that she had loved her young master but too well, all the better perhaps because he could not or would not make an honest woman of the fair leman (sweetheart or mistress) by making the beauteous lass his bride; however that may

*Bottrell goes on to explain that this once-great seat of the Levelis, or Lovells, had fallen into decay well before his time. The estate was inherited by three separate families: two decided to demolish their part of the great mansion; the third family incorporated their portion into their new residence. As he remarks, the remainder served as a quarry for the neighbourhood for many years afterwards, and pieces of finely carved masonry may still be found here in the fabric of pig-sties or other farm outbuildings.

be, the favourite servant would never leave the place in life nor in death, but always remained here in spite of all that the lady of the mansion and her lawfully begotten family could do to dislodge her.

Many generations had passed away before she was finally put to rest in a small upper room of the malt-house wing, by being bound over by some learned priest to the task of carding a number of fleeces of black wool until it became white, and to spin as much from the same (without breaking the yarn) as would make her a shroud. Long after the spirit was put to rest, 'tis said that the maltsman, having to remain up late one October night to turn the malt, fill up the casks of fermenting ale, mash more malt for a new brewing, and for other work that requires to be attended to by night as well as by day in good careful malting and brewing, heard, when up in the chamber turning the malt, more than common racket with the spinning-wheel and the clicking of cards in making the rolls of wool. The maltsman was a jolly blade, 'who could drain his bowl, like a right honest soul'. He cared but little for ghosts, and thought, by the sounds being so natural, that more than one person in real flesh and blood must be working overhead. He did no better nor worse than make three taps on the planching overhead with the end of his shovel. The roar of the turn and click of the cards that instant stopped and the three knocks answered by three louder from above. Then he tapped the floor seven times with his knuckles. These were returned in the same gentle way. Now he was persuaded that some of the lasses who belonged to the house had found out a secret passage, or stair in some garret or closet adjacent, by which they could reach the room over, and that they were then spinning for a wager, or perhaps some wool that they had purloined for themselves was there spun by the sly.

The man had no thought of fear, as he could still hear, late as it was, the boisterous mirth of the huntsmen and some of the hard-drinking guests who caroused in the distant hall, and, as soon as he had finished his work about the malt, he knocked again for the third time with the end of the hilt against the floor overhead. Again the spinning ceased, and the same number of blows, like a signal, were returned. 'Stop a bit, and I am coming,' said he. A moment after what seemed two hollow voices replied, 'Come, come, come.' As the man descended the outside stone steps from the malt-chamber to the brew-house he saw the light shining bright and natural-like, over against the yew hedge, and on the plants in that part of the garden. Though he and the rest of the servants had often been cautioned never to meddle with the haunted chamber, or ill-luck would befall them, yet, finding when he came into the court a ladder left against the wall, like as if some evil spirit had placed it there to tempt him to his doom, he fixed the ladder to rest on the roof of some low building which joined the towering gable, and contrived to place it so that the top nearly reached the wisht-looking little ivy-buried window. As he mounted the ladder he heard shrieks of laughter, which he thought might come from some of the servants' bedrooms at no great distance off; but when he reached the top and looked in through the window all sounds had ceased – even the never-ending dismal night-call of the owls was no longer heard, and the flitting bats had disappeared.

He could make out but little at first in the weak glimmering blue light within, which came neither from lamp nor candle that he could see; but from a confused mass of things on the floor in the middle of the small room he saw what he at last made out to be an elderly woman dressed in a ordinary bedgown. All her long skeleton body was closely wrapped and folded up in a sheet, except her long bony arms, that kept on wearily and ceaselessly working a pair of cards, on a handful of black wool. He saw large heaps of black wool all around her, and piles of grey dust, or the tormented wool that never lost all its colour, between him and what he took to be a chest, till the dust made him cough, and then the apparition raised its ghastly head, and the shroud fell off the face that looked as though it had been long in the grave. Deep in the holes of the skull, in the places where the eyes once shone, were lurid balls of fire, that shot out their light like the rays from a dark lantern, and left all else in gloom. When the glaring balls were turned on the man he felt the marrow of his bones pierced as with darts of fire. He had neither the power to move nor to speak. Then the ghastly corpse turned its fiery eyes around and rested them on the chest, but he saw then by their light that it was a white coffin. In the midst of the wool a small treadle-turn, like old women use for spinning flax, stood beside the half-open coffin. From within it arose the figure of a younger and fairer corpse, but all covered with purple spots, like poison-marks. Pointing, and looking at the man as she arose, she said, 'Here is room enow for thee.' Then both the ghostly forms glided towards the window like things floating in the air, and shook the dust from their shrouds and winding-sheets in the intruder's face. Lurid streams of fiery light from the eyes of the apparitions, choking dust from their shrouds, and the sickening smell of grave-clothes, made the man become so dizzy, sick and faint, that he fell from the ladder, broke his ribs by a fall on a grindstone in the corner of the court, and crawled into the beer-house, where he was found senseless the next morning, and could only be roused up long enough to tell how he came by his mishap; then he shook his head, groaned, kicked, sneezed and died.

The old women put it down that the younger ghost with the purple-spotted face must have been another of the master's favourites: some fair child of sixteen, sent off by her jealous mistress with a cup of night-shade decoction, or a bowl of hemlock broth. Long after the brew-house wing was a roofless ruin these troublesome spirits might be heard wailing all the night long.

A Legend of Porthgwarra

Old folks also called this place, one of the most picturesque and secluded nooks that may anywhere be found, the Sweethearts' Cove, from a tradition of its having been the scene of a tragical love story. . . .

Far back in old times the son of a fisherman who lived at Porthgwarra was in the service of a rich farmer of Roskestal. He courted his master's only daughter, who, almost from her childhood, loved the young man with a strength of affection beyond her control. The youngster, William, being of a roving turn, often went to sea for many months in the summer, and although he was then most wanted on the farm, his master always took him back again when sailors were paid off and merchant ships laid up during the stormy winter season. It was his old master's great delight to sit with his daughter and neighbours around the blazing fire on a winter's night and hear William tell of the strange things he had beheld on the ocean and in foreign lands. William himself was a wonder of perfection, past compare in the eyes of his sweetheart, Nancy. She admired him for his stalwart form, for his strange adventures on sea and land, and for the rare presents he brought her home. The farmer, too, liked him just as if he had been his own son, yet it never entered his head that his only daughter would ever think of the dashing and careless young seaman as her lover. Yet her mother, more sharp sighted, soon discovered that her fair Nancy was much in love with their serving-man. When William was gone to sea the dame upbraided her with want of proper pride and self-respect till she had fretted her almost to death's door. 'What a fool thou must be,' said she, 'to throw thyself away, or to hanker after one so much beneath thy degree, when thy good looks and dower make thee a match for the richest farmer's son in the West Country; think if you wed a poor sailor how you will be scorned by all your kith and kin.' Nancy replied, 'But little care I for relations' reproach or good will, and sink or swim if ever I marry it shall be the man I love who is able to work and win.'

The dame prevailed on her husband, much against his will, however, not to take the sailor to live there when he returned home again, and she – watching her opportunity – slammed the door in his face and told him he should nevermore harbour beneath her roof. But the father fearing his only child would pine to death, told her and her lover that if he would try his fortune by a voyage to the Indies for three years, when he returned, poor or rich, if he and Nancy were in the same mind, they might be wedded for all he cared.

That being agreed on, William got a berth in a merchantman bound for a long voyage, took friendly leave of his old master, and the night before his ship was ready to sail he and Nancy met, and he assured the sorrowing damsel that in three years or less she might expect him to land in Porthgwarra with plenty of riches, and he would marry her at home or fetch her away and make her his bride.

Three years passed during which the old dame had done her utmost to persuade her daughter to become the wife of some rich farmer – for true it was, as she said, Nancy might have had her choice of the best – yet coaxing and reproaches were powerless to shake the maid's constancy. When three years and many months were gone without any tidings of William, she became very melancholy – perhaps crazy – from hope deferred, and took to wandering about the cliffs in all weathers, by day and by night.

On the headland, called Hella Point, which stretches far out west of the cove, there is a high overhanging rock almost on the verge of the cliff, which shelters, on its southern side, a patch of greensward, mostly composed of cliff-pinks; this spot used to be known as Fair Nancy's bed. There she would pass hours by day and often whole nights watching vessels that came within her ken, hoping to see her lover land from every one that hove in sight, and to be the first to hail him with joyful greetings in the cove. At length the poor maiden had to be watched and followed for fear that in her night wanderings she might fall over the cliff or drown herself in a fit of despair.

One moonlit winter's night, when in her chamber indulging her grief, she heard William's voice just under her window, saying, 'Sleepest thou, sweetheart; awaken and come hither, love: my boat awaits us in the cove, thou must come this night or never be my bride.'

'My sweet William come at last, I'll be with thee in an instant,' she replied.

Nancy's aunt Prudence, who lodged in the same room, heard William's request and his sweetheart's answer; looking out of the window she saw the sailor, just under, dripping wet and deathly pale. An instant after – glancing round into the chamber, and seeing Nancy leave it – she dressed, in all haste, and followed her. Aunt Prudence, running down the cliff lane at her utmost speed, kept the lovers in sight some time, but could not overtake them, for they seemed to glide down the rocky pathway leading to Porthgwarra as if borne on the wind, till they disappeared in the glen.

At the fisherman's door, however, she again caught a glimpse of them passing over the rocks towards a boat which floated off in the cove. She then ran out upon the How – as the high ground projecting into the cove is called – just in time to see them on a large flat rock beside the boat, when a fog rolling on over the sea, shrouded them from her view. She hailed them but heard no reply. In a few minutes the mist cleared away, bright moonlight again shone on the water, but the boat and lovers had disappeared.

Then she heard mermaids singing a low sweet melody, and saw many of them sporting on the water under Hella; that was nothing new, however, for the rocks and sawns (caverns) bordering this headland were always noted as favourite resorts of these death-boding syrens, whose wild unearthly strains were wont, before tempests, to be heard resounding along Peden-Penwith shores.

By daybreak the old fisherman came to Rosketal and told the

farmer that he hoped to find his son there, for, about midnight, he saw him at the bedside, looking ghastly pale; he stayed but a moment, and merely said, 'Farewell father and mother, I am come for my bride and must hasten away,' when he vanished like a spirit. It all seemed to the old man uncertain as a dream; he did not know if it had been his own son in the body or a token of his death.

In the afternoon, ere they had ceased wondering and making search for Nancy, a young mariner came to the fisherman's dwelling and told him that he was the chief officer of his son's ship, then at the Mount with a rich cargo from the Indies, bound for another port; but put in there because his son – their captain – when off Porthgwarra, where he intended to land last night, eager to see his native place, went aloft, and the ship rolling he missed his holdfast of the shrouds, fell overboard and sunk before she could be brought-to or any assistance rendered.

All knew then that William's ghost had taken Nancy to a phantom boat, and a watery grave was the lovers' bridal-bed. Thus their rash vows of constancy, even in death, were fulfilled, and their sad story caused Porthgwarra to be known as the Sweethearts' Cove.

The Smugglers of Penrose

What remains of the old mansion of Penrose, in Sennen, stands on a low and lonely site at the head of a narrow valley through which a millbrook winds, with many abrupt turns, for about three miles, thence to Penberth Cove. So late as forty years ago it was one of those antique, mysterious-looking buildings which most people regard with a degree of interest that no modern structure inspires; the upper storey only – with its mullioned windows, pointed gables and massive chimney-stacks – was just seen over the ivy-covered walls of courts and gardens that surrounded it.

There was, however, a certain gloomy air about the ruinous walls and neglected gardens embowered in aged trees which might have conduced to such unaccountable stories of apparitions and other unnatural occurrences as were said to have taken place there.

Some three or four centuries ago it was the property and residence of an ancient family of the same name; little more is known of these old Penroses than what can be gathered from wild traditions related by the winter's hearth. The following among many others was often recounted by old folks of the west.

About 300 years ago the owner of Penrose was a younger son who had been brought up to a seafaring life, which he continued to follow till his elder brothers died unmarried and left him heir to the family estate; then, preferring a life on the wave, he kept a well-armed fast-sailing craft for fair-trading, or what is now called smuggling. She was manned with as brave a crew as could be picked out of the West Country; most of them are said to been the Squire's poor relations. A favourite cousin called William Penrose – who had been his shipmate for years – was captain of the merry men all.

The Squire often took trips to France and other places whence his goods were bought, and it said that in his days the Penrose crew were never concerned in any piratical jobs; though we know that about that time smuggler, privateer and pirate meant very much the same thing.

Penrose and his seamen passed but little time on shore except in the depth of winter; yet the board in his hall was always furnished with good substantial fare and the best of liquors, free for all-comers. Over a few years, when the good man was left a widower, with an only child – a boy about seven or eight – he seemed to dislike the very sight of land, for then, even winter, with his little son, his cousin William, and two or three old sailors, he would stay out at sea for weeks together, leaving the care of his farms and household to a younger brother and an old reeve or bailiff.

In returning from one of these trips, on a dark winter's night, their boat struck on Cowloe and became a wreck. The Squire swam into Sennen Cove with his boy, and in endeavouring to save his crew got drowned himself.

The only remaining brother, known as Jan of Penrose, constituted himself sole guardian of the heir and master of the place and property. Now this Jan hated all whom his late brother favoured; and in consequence of his ill-will William Penrose left the West Country – for the sea it was supposed – but whither he wandered was unknown, as no tidings of him were received in the west.

The new master, however, soon got a large smuggling craft and manned her with a crew who cared but little what they did for gold or an exciting life; being well armed they feared nothing that sailed the ocean. Jan of Penrose never went to sea, but gave the command to a wretch – known to have been a pirate – who was cast on Gwenvor sands from his ship wrecked in Whitesand Bay, on the night that the good Squire Penrose was drowned. This pirate-smuggler and his desperate crew boarded many a rich merchantman going up Channel, from which they appropriated whatsoever they pleased, and sent all who opposed them to the other world by water.

There was no Preventive Service then to be any check on our free trade. If Revenue Cutters came near our western land, their crews dreaded to fall in with Cornish fair-traders more than our smugglers feared the King's Men. As for riding-officers, they would ride anywhere rather than on the cliff, when beacon fires blazed from the cairns of dark nights to guide fair-traders' boats into coves. People came from all over the country to purchase the goods, safely stowed in vaults and other hiding-places about Penrose; and in winter the crew spent much of their time there in drunken rioting with all the reckless youngsters of the neighbourhood.

After the good Squire was drowned his brother appeared to show every kindness to the orphan heir; yet it was remarked that the child seemed instinctively to avoid his uncle and the captain, who consorted much together when the smugglers were ashore. Whenever the boy could elude the old steward's vigilance he would go away alone to the rocks in Sennen Cove where his father was drowned, or shut himself up for hours in his father's bedroom, or wander about other parts of the gloomy north wing, which was almost in ruins and seldom entered by other inmates.

One winter's day, the ground being covered with snow, Penrose's people and many others of the neighbourhood joined for a wolf-hunt. Traditions say that in those times terrible havoc was made on flocks by these fierce beasts, and that children were sometimes carried off by them when hard pressed by hunger. Neither Jan Penrose nor the captain went to the chase; when at night the game-laden hunters returned and blew their bugle-horns, they remarked with surprise that the young heir – who was a great favourite – did not, as was his wont, come into the court to meet them. The boy was sought for in every place whither it was thought he might have strayed. His uncle seemed most distressed, and continued the fruitless search until it

was surmised the the child must have missed his way in returning from Sennen Cove, wandered out under Escols Cliff, and there got drowned by the flowing tide, being carried out to sea on the ebb.

After this, Jan of Penrose, having all his own, became more riotously debauched than ever; and his gang having taken strange aversion to their captain, the latter left and was no more seen in the west.

The tapestry chamber and all the northern wing was shut up, or unoccupied, as it had the reputation of being haunted. None of the servants nor even the devil-may-care smugglers would venture into it after nightfall, when unearthly shrieks would be heard there, and strange lights seen flashing through the casements till near morning. Lights were also often seen in an orchard just below the town-place when no one was there.

One night of the following Christmas, while a large company was assembled at Penrose keeping high festival after a day's hunt, loud knocking was heard at the green-court door, and soon after a servant conducted into the hall an elderly wayfaring man who requested a night's shelter from the snowstorm. Jan Penrose received the wanderer with hospitable courtesy, and charged the old steward to provide him with good cheer. The guests continued their glee and paid but little attention to him, for begging homeless pilgrims were all too plenty here at that time.

When he had completed his feast at the table, and watched, for a while, the antics of a company of strolling players; he withdrew and told the steward that he felt weary after his long walk through the snow and would be glad to lie down. If all the beds were occupied he would repose on a settle by the fireside, for a few hours only, as he intended to leave early in the morning. The old man replied that he feared any other accommodation in his power to offer was not such as he might desire – although the house was large with ample bedrooms for more guests than it now contained – because a great part of the northern end was shut up for a reason that the inmates did not like to talk about. Yet as he believed the pilgrim to be a prudent man, who was, no doubt, learned in ghostly matters, he was glad to unburden his own mind and have the visitor's counsel, with his prayers for the unquiet spirits that disturbed the place. Then he told how many of the upper rooms, though well furnished, were unused and falling to ruin on account of the unnatural sounds and sights before mentioned. To which the stranger answered that as he had a mind at ease he had no reason to dread any ghostly visitants; if the steward would conduct him to a room in the haunted wing he did not fear for his rest.

The old steward, taking a lamp, led the way to the tapestry chamber – being the best room in that part of the mansion. A faggot of dry ash-wood – already laid in the large open fireplace – was soon in a blaze, and the room well aired and somewhat comfortable. He then brought in bread, meat and wine that the guest might take more refreshment during the night. After returning with more wood and bog-turf to keep in the fire, he bade the guest good-night, sweet rest and pleasant dreams.

The storm had ceased and a full moon, shining on newly fallen snow, made it almost as light as day. He opened the casement and looked into the court, where he saw a company of young men and women passing out singly and in silence. The visitor, being well acquainted with West Country customs, knew – as this was Twelfth Night – that the object of this silent procession was to work some of the many spells, usually practised at this time, for the purpose of gaining a knowledge of their future destiny with respect to what they regarded as the most important of all events – marriage and death.*

The pilgrim had not sat long, looking out of the open casement, when he saw the company of young men and maidens come running back, apparently in great fright. The doors were all immediately slammed to, the noisy mirth and music suddenly ceased in the hall. The house, in a few moments, was shrouded in thick fog; all was as still as death about the place for some minutes, then a noise was heard like the distant roaring and moaning of the sea in a storm.

These ocean sounds seemed to approach nearer and nearer every instant, until the waves were heard as if breaking and surging around the house. In the wailing wind was heard the noise of oars rattling in

*Many persons, who were anxious to know their future fate with regard to love and marriage, or for mere fun, were in the habit of assembling on Twelfth Night in a farmhouse kitchen which had a large open fireplace – used for burning furze and turf. A fire was laid that would make plenty of embers and hot ashes, such being required for working the spells; then each person touched the 'cravel' (mantle-stone) with his or her forehead, and departed in single file and silence, which was required to be observed, until, having gathered the rushes and ivy leaves, they returned and again touched the cravel with their heads. The procession was often waylaid or followed by some who tried to make the spell-workers break silence. If any of them spoke they had to return and again touch the cravel.

Those who wished to know their own luck in love or marriage, or that of different couples who were said to be sweethearts, placed in the ashes two pieces of rush – named or intended for the respective parties; if both rushes burnt kindly together, those they represented would be married. As the pairs were consumed, united or parted, such would be the course of their love. The one that burnt longest would outlive the other. When it was decided who were to be married together an ivy leaf was cast into the fire, and the number of cracks it made in burning told the years to pass before the couple would be wed. Then two leaves for the wedded pair were buried in the hot ashes, and the cracks they made showed how many children the happy couple would be blessed with. Other presages, which afforded much amusement, were drawn from the behaviour and appearance of rushes and ivy leaves – or lovers and married folks – in their fiery bed.

Meanwhile, old people – who in general were the most anxious to know if they or others were destined to live or die during the ensuing year – drew an ivy leaf for each person, either named or thought of, through a gold ring, and cast the leaves into a vessel of spring water, which was placed on the hearthstone and left there over night. Next morning, the leaves that were found to have turned black, or to be specked with red spots like blood, showed that those for whom they were intended would be dead ere next Twelfth Night. The blood spots betokened a violent end. (Bottrell) their rowlocks for another instant; then as of the oars being hastily cast into a boat. This was followed by the hollow voices of the smugglers, drowned with the old Squire, hailing their own names, as drowned men's ghosts are said to do when they want the assistance of the living to procure them rest.

All this time the green-court appeared as if filled with the sea, and one could hear the breakers roaring as when standing on a cliff in a storm. The buildings and trees surrounding the mansion disappeared as if sunk into the ground. At length the surging of waves and other sounds died away until they were heard like the 'calling of cleeves' before a tempest.

The steward had told the stranger of these noises and appearances, which had become frequent of late, to the great terror of the household; but he gave little heed to the old man's tales, thinking that such visions were merely the creations of weak brains diseased by strong potions. Having a clear conscience, he feared nothing evil in what appeared to him an unaccountable mystery, and, having told his beads, he committed himself to the care of the good spirits.

However, his repose did not remain undisturbed for long. The brave man was rather soothed than alarmed by the plaintive melody that he suddenly heard, until there was a change in the harmonious strains, which grew more distinct. Mingled with them were the tones of loved and familiar voices, calling, 'William Penrose, arise and avenge the murder of thy cousin's son!'

Casting a glance towards the window – whence the sound proceeded – he saw just within it the apparition of a beautiful boy in white raiment. A light which surrounded it showed the countenance of the lost heir of Penrose. At the same time the room was filled with an odour like that of sweet spring flowers.

The apparition, coming nearer, told how he had been murdered by the pirate-captain of the smugglers on the grand hunting day; and how his uncle had given the pirate a great quantity of gold to do the bloody deed – that he had been buried in the orchard under an apple-tree, that would be known, even in winter, by its blasted appearance, that the murderer was then in Plymouth, keeping a public-house, the situation of which was so plainly described by the spirit that William Penrose would have no difficulty in finding it, and so bring the murderer to justice by means of such proofs of his crime as would be found beneath the blasted tree.

William Penrose having promised to perform all according to the

wishes of the departed, music was again heard and the spirit gradually disappeared in a cloud of light. After this he fell into a deep slumber.

When he awoke he sought out the old steward and asked him to accompany him a short distance on his journey. Before they parted the stranger disclosed himself, to the old man's great delight, to be the long-lamented William Penrose. He told him that he was about to undertake a long journey for the repose of the dead, and that he would return when he had accomplished his mission. Then he bade the steward adieu, without speaking of the apparition or the cause of the disturbances in the mansion.

William Penrose, having arrived in the ancient town of Plymouth, and entered the mean public-house to which he had been directed by the apparition, saw the person he sought lying stretched by the fireside in a squalid apartment that served as a kitchen, guest-chamber and sleeping room. The former pirate-captain looked like a deserter from a churchyard. The face of this child-murderer was the colour of one long in the tomb with but little sign of life except in the baleful glare of his sunken eyes. William Penrose with much difficulty induced the 'wisht-looking' object to converse and, for a while, led him to talk of the West Country, then of Sennen. From that he spoke of Penrose, and asked him if he knew, in Penrose orchard, a certain apple-tree which he pointedly described, whereupon the inn-keeper exclaimed, 'I am a dead man.'

And so he was. For as he finished his terrible confession, in which he told that it was not the gold given him by Jan of Penrose that brought him to murder the boy, but his thwarted love for the child's mother which had generated in him an everlasting hatred of the family, he died with contortions of agony which turned his features into a mockey of anything human.

When William Penrose returned to Penrose and made himself known, to the great joy of old servants and others, he found that what was thought to be merely the gloomy and morose temper of its master frequently made him shun all society, and wander about the hills and cliffs and other solitary places, for days and nights together. No one either loved, feared or cared enough about the surly man to pay him any regard. He was absent then in one of his melancholy moods and William, with the steward and other old trusted servants, removed the child's remains from beneath the blasted tree to Sennen church-yard. Out of respect to the honourable old family little was said or known about the sad occurrence.

Jan of Penrose was no more seen alive in the old mansion, for the same night that his nephew's remains were buried in consecrated ground, he hanged himself in the malt-house, and he haunted it long after.

Following the spirit's injunction William Penrose had still to find and remove the bodies of the old Squire and his crew. Now it is supposed that they were 'sanded' – that is sunk in the moist sand and covered by it during a flowing tide – near Gwenvor Cove, because corpse-lights had frequently been seen, and the drowned sailors had been heard there hailing their own names. Thus they were found the next day. Their remains were laid to repose, with all holy rites, in an ancient burying-ground near Chapel Idne where the wind and waves sing their everlasting requiem in music they loved well when alive. . .

William Penrose, now heir-at-law of the Bartons of Penrose, Brew and other farms in the West Country – disliking to live in the place connected with such melancholy events – gave up his rights of heirship to another branch of the family; resumed his pilgrim's staff; and was supposed to have died in the Holy Land.

The Penroses still in the west are said to be descended from a younger branch of the ancient family of Sennen, with whom the Pendreas or Pendars were intermarried.

The family of Jones purchased the Penroses' West Country property, and it remained in their possession until the beginning of the last century. We hear again of smugglers being kept in pay by the last Jones of Penrose, and by others who succeeded him. From the facilities afforded by this secluded place for concealing contraband goods, it was always noted as a favourite resort for western fair-traders.

Many people about the Land's End believe the old mansion was always haunted; and it is said this was the principal reason for taking down and rebuilding a portion of it a few years since.

Tregagle

One may almost every day hear West Country folks make allusion to Tregagle; for instance, a squalling child is called a Tregagle; and to a blusterer they often say, 'Hold thy bleaton, thee art worse than Tregagle's roaran before a storm.'

Our vague traditions represent him as having been a most unscrupulous lawyer, and say that he rose from low estate by taking bribes to lose his poorer client's cases, by bearing or procuring false witnesses, forging documents relating to the bequest of property, and other nefarious transactions which brought him riches and power.

All our western legends agree, however, in stating that the particular business which was the cause of his being 'called from the grave' was this:

A man who resided in the eastern part of the county lent a sum of money to another without receiving bond or note or anything for security, as the transaction was witnessed by Tregagle, for whom the money was borrowed, and who died before the money was repaid. Soon after Tregagle's death the lender demanded his money and the debtor denied ever having received it.

The case was brought before the court at Bodmin assizes, and when the plaintiff said that Tregagle was the only witness the defendant denied it with an oath, and exclaimed, 'If Tregagle ever saw it I wish to God that Tregagle may come and declare it.'

The words were no sooner uttered than Tregagle stood before the court and, pointing to the man, said, 'I can no more be a false witness. Thou hast had the money and found it easy to bring me from the grave but thou will not find it so easy to put me away.'

Wherever the terrified man moved about the court Tregagle followed him; he begged the judge and long-robed gentlemen to relieve him from the spirit. 'That's thy business,' said they, one and all, 'thou hast brought him, thou may'st get him laid.'

The man returned home, but whithersover he went Tregagle followed, and would seldom quit his side or let him rest by night or by day. He repaid the borrowed money, gave much in alms, and sought to get rid of the spirit by the aid of parsons, conjurors, and other wise men, before they succeeded in binding it, for a while, to empty Dosmery Pool with a limpet shell that had a hole in its bottom.

Having soon finished that task, he returned to the man that brought him from his grave, and followed and tormented him worse than before, until he procured the help of other exorcists who were more astute. The first thing they did was to draw a circle, out in the town-place, and put the man to stand within it. The spirit then took the form of a black bull and tried to get at him with horns and hoofs, but the man was safe within the line traced. A parson continued reading all the time; at first the holy words of power made him furious; by turns, he bellowed like a mad bull, hissed like an adder, or roared like a wild beast that he might be heard for miles away. Yet, by degrees, Tregagle became as gentle as a lamb, and allowed the spirit-quellers to bind with a new hempen cord, and to lead him far away to Gwenvor Cove. There they doomed him to make a truss of sand, to be bound with ropes made of the same material, and carry it up to Carn Olva.

Tregagle was a long while at his tiresome task without being able to accomplish it, until it came to a very cold winter when, one hard frosty night, by taking water from Velan Dreath brook, and pouring it over his truss, he caused it to freeze together and bore it in triumph to Carn Olva.

He then flew back to the man who raised him, and he would have torn him to pieces, but, by good luck, he happened to have in his arms an innocent young child, so the spirit could not harm him. Without delay the terrified man sent for the nearest parson, who, however, was not able, alone, to cope with Tregagle; the most he could do was to prevent him from harming the man until other spirit-quellers were brought to his assistance, with whose aid the furious spirit was again bound, led away to Gwenvor, and required to undertake the same task, without going near fresh water.

So Tregagle was matched at last, for he is still there on the shore of Whitesand Bay vainly trying to make his truss of sand; and he is frequently heard roaring for days before a northerly storm comes to scatter his work.

Traditions of Porthcurno

Not long since a general belief prevailed in the western parishes that in ancient times Porthcurno was the principal port of Cornwall and that, until the Cove became 'sanded up', there was sufficient depth of water to float the largest ships then made to the foot of an old caunce (paved road) which may still be seen.

One old story ascribes the choking of Porthcurno and Parchapel (Porth Chapel) to the mischievous spirit Tregagle, who, on the very same night that he succeeded in making his truss of sand with the frozen waters of the stream at Gwenvor, took his way along the coast towards Helston, to revisit and torment those who raised him from the grave. By way of showing his exultation at having completed his task, or for mere devilry perhaps, he swept all the sand out of Nanjizal and around Pedn-pen-with into Porthcurno and adjacent coves, without letting any enter Porthgwarra. Another tradition says that sweeping the sand from Nanjizal to the east of Tol-Pedn was assigned to Tregagle as a separate task.

There is also a very old belief that spectre ships frequently visit Porthcurno, both before and since its navigable channel became filled with sand, and that they were often seen sailing up and down the valley, over dry land the same as on the sea. These naval apparitions were, in olden times, regarded as 'tokens' that enemies were about to make a descent; the number of phantom vessels foreboded the sea-robbers' approaching force.

This presage of yore was held for truth by many old folks but lately deceased; yet latterly it has somehow changed its character and become connected with the history of a person who, little more than a hundred years ago, lived in a lone house called Chygwidden, about a mile inland from Porthcurno. This comparatively modern story also accounts for the sand shifting, and has appropriated old traditions that had no connection therewith.

It relates that, long ago, Chygwidden was the chief dwelling-place of a family who flourished in St Levan for a few generations and then all its branches became so reduced, through riotous living, as to be obliged to mortgage and sell much of their freehold lands. The eldest and only son, by a former wife, of old Martin T—, who lived there, took to the seafaring life when about twenty, on account of cruel treatment received from his drunken father and a step-dame several years younger than himself. On leaving he vowed that he would never return while one lived who then darkened his father's doors.

Many years passed, and as no tidings had been received of young Martin, as he was still called, most persons believed him dead. In the meantime, his father, the step-dame, and her children, having all died within a few years of each other, a distant relative, as heir-at-law, had taken possession of what little property remained, and lived in Chygwidden.

Some ten years after the decease of all who had lived under old Martin's roof when his eldest son was driven thence, a large ship heave-to within a mile of Porthcurno on a fine afternoon in harvest time. People working in fields near the cliff noticed the unusual circumstance and saw a boat leave the ship with two men, who landed in Porthcurno with several chests and other goods, and the ship proceeded on her course. It was evident that one of those who came on shore was well acquainted with the place, as he struck at once into a pathway over the cliff which led, by a short cut, to Rospeltha, where he made himself known as young Martin T— and procured horses and other help to take several chests and heavy bales to Chygwidden.

There was great rejoicing when it was known that the wanderer had at length returned to claim his own. His kinsfolk – a younger man and his sister Eleanor, a damsel in her teens – were ready to resign possession, but Martin then cared little for house or land, and told them to keep the place and welcome, for all he desired was to have a home there for himself and his comrade while they remained, which he thought would be for only a short spell. His tastes had changed with change of scene. The place that once he had deemed the fairest on earth – but then he had seen no more of it than was visible from the nearest high hill – now appeared dreary; and the people whom – those of his family excepted – he once thought the best in the world now seemed a forlorn set of consequential, grimly religious nobodies to him, and above all to his mate, who by the by, requires more particular notice than we have yet bestowed on him.

Martin found the people, also, much altered from what they were in his youthful days, for about the time of his return a new sect had sprung up whose members, professing uncommon godliness, decried our ancient games and merry-makings, which were wont on holidays to unite all ages and classes. Their condemnation caused them to fall into disuse; and, on account of the censorious and intolerant spirit that then prevailed, there was much less heartiness and cordial intercourse among neighbours than formerly.

In a short time, however, Martin, now called by most persons 'The Captain', became reconciled – one cannot say attached – to his native place and the 'humdrum West Country folks', as he styled them, who marvelled at his riches and the change which had taken place in his outward mien and manner. Yet the homely people's surprise at the alteration in Martin was nothing to their wonder, allied to fear, excited by his dusky companion or slave, for no one knew in what relation they stood to each other.

This stranger was seen to be a robust man, about thirty years of age apparently, with a swarthy complexion, many shades darker than the captain's Spanish-mahogany tinted skin. Martin called this man José or mate, and he rarely spoke a word of English (though he could when he pleased) or addressed anyone but Martin, with whom he conversed in some outlandish lingo which seemed more natural to the captain than his native tongue. A tantalising mystery surrounded the dark 'outlander'; for his master or friend would never answer any queries respecting him. He was almost equally silent with regard to buccaneering or other adventures, and rarely spoke of anything that occurred either at home or abroad during his absence. The two strange beings often came to high words and even to blows, but they would never allow anyone to meddle in their quarrels. When Martin was drunk and off his guard he would now and then ease his mind by swearing at his mate in plain English, or grumble at him in the same, to the effect that he had risked his life and spent a fortune to save him from being hanged at the yard-arm. 'Discontented devil of a blackamoor', he would say, 'why canst thou not be satisfied to live here? Thou art bound to me body and soul; and do I not indulge thee with everything gold can purchase?'

José would sometimes murmur, 'Avast there; all our gold and diamonds can't procure us here the bright sunshine and joyous people, nor the rich fruits and wine, of my native clime.' But usually, his gloomy looks or fiery glances soon recalled Martin to his senses. It was remarked that after these outbursts of passion he was for a long while like the humble slave of his mate.

The boat in which they landed was kept at Porthcurno, except for short spells during stormy times of the year, when she was put into Penberth or Porthgwarra for greater safety; and, weeks together, they would remain out at sea night and day till their provisions were used; then they would come in, their craft laden with fish, and this cargo was free to all-comers. Stormy weather seldom drove them to land; they seemed to delight in a tempest.

Before winter came they procured a good number of hounds, and a great part of the hunting season was passed by them in coursing over all parts of the West Country. Often on winter's nights, people far away would be frightened by hearing or seeing these two wild-looking hunters and their dogs chasing over some lone moor, and they gave rise to many a story of Old Nick and his headless hounds.

When tired of the chase, weeks were often spent at a public-house in Buryan churchtown. Martin treated one and all and scattered gold around him like chaff. The tawny mate, however, at times restrained Martin's lavish expenditure, took charge of his money-chests, and refused him the keys. José would occasionally condescend to express his wishes to Eleanor, who was mistress of the rare establishment. She understood and humoured the pair, who took pleasure in decking her in the richest stuffs and jewels that their chests contained.

After being at home a year or so the captain had a large half-decked boat built, and several rocks removed in Porthcurno to make a safer

place in which to moor her. They then took longer trips, and were not seen in Chygwidden for months running.

At length Martin perceived tokens of death, or what he took as such, and made his man swear that when he saw signs of near dissolution he would take him off to sea, let him die there, and send him to rest at the ocean's bottom. He also bound his kinsman by oath not to oppose his wishes, and invoked a curse on anyone who would lay his dust beside the remains of those who had driven him to range the wide world like a vagabond. They might have complied with his strange desires, but ere they could be carried out he died in a hammock, suspended in his bedroom.

Now there comes a mystery, that is not likely to be cleared up. It was known that a coffin – followed by the cousins, José, and the dogs, was taken to St Levan's churchyard and buried near the ground in which Martin's family lie. But it was rumoured that the coffin merely contained earth to make weight.

The following night, however, the dark 'outlander' had two chests conveyed to Porthcurno, the largest of which was said to contain the remains of his friend, and the other money and valuables which belonged to himself. The chests placed on board the half-decked vessel, José, Eleanor, and the favourite dog embarked, waited for the tide to rise, and then put to sea. But no one remained at the cove to behold their departure, and no more of them was seen in the west.

The boat was scarcely a league to sea ere a tempest arose and continued with great fury for nearly a week; and, although it was winter, the sky of nights was all ablaze with lightning and the days as dark as nights. During the storm Porthcurno was choked with sand, and no boat could be kept there since.

The tempest had scarcely lulled when an apparition of Martin's craft would drive into Porthcurno against wind and tide; oft-times she came in the dusk of evening, and, without stopping at the cove, took her course up over the old caunce towards Porth Chapel; thence she sailed away, her keel just skimming the ground, or many yards above it, as she passed over hill and dale until she arrived at Chygwidden.

The barque was generally shrouded in mist, and one could rarely get a glimpse of her deck on which the shadowy figures of two men, a woman and a dog, were beheld now and then. This ship of the dead, with her ghostly crew, hovered over the town-place a moment, then bore away to a croft on the farm, and vanished near a rock where a large sum of foreign coins was disinterred many years ago, so it is said. Of late the ghostly ship has not been known to have entered Porthcurno, and on account of innovations recently effected there she may nevermore be seen at that ancient port.

It may be observed that traditions of phantom ships sailing overland were common to many places near the Land's End with which no stories are connected; these appearances were merely supposed to forebode tempests and wrecks. The few incidents which form the groundwork of the above legend occurred but little more than a century before it was related to me by an aged farm labourer of St Levan – yet in that short space it has assumed such a mystic garb that the simple and true story is all but hidden.

The Wrecker and the Death Ship

More than a hundred years ago a dark strange man appeared in St Just; no one knew whence he came, but it was supposed that he was put ashore from a pirate ship, by way of marooning him.

He did not appear to want for money as he soon rented a small, lone, tenement near the shore and married a widow of the neighbourhood. People wondered, for a long while, how so many vessels got wrecked under the cliff that bordered the stranger's farm. At length it was discovered that on dark winter nights – when honest folks were abed – he made it his practice to fasten a lantern to the neck of a horse, which he had hobbled, by tying down its head to a fore-leg; then he drove the horse along near the cliff, and the lantern from its motion would be taken for a vessel's stern-light.

Consequently those on board ships sailing by, expecting to find plenty of sea room, would come right in and be wrecked on the rocks. Any of their crews that escaped a watery grave the wretch would knock on the head with an axe, or cut off their hand when they tried to grasp the rocks.

He lived long and became rich by his sin. At length, however, the time came for the fiend to claim his own. When he was dying his awful shrieks were heard far away as he cried, 'Do save me from the Devil, and the sailors, there, looking to tear me to pieces.' Several parsons and other pious folks were sent for: all those of the neighbourhood readily came, for the dying sinner was rich.

Though it was in harvest time and high day, the old wrecker's chamber became, at times, as dark as night. The parsons saw the Devil in the room when others could not; by their reading they drove him to take many shapes, but for all that he would not be put out; at last, when he took the form of a fly and buzzed about the dying wretch, they saw it was in vain for them to try any longer. During the time the exorcists were engaged the chamber seemed, by the sound, to be filled with the sea splashing around the bed; waves were heard as if surging and breaking against the house, though it was a good bit inland.

While this was taking place at the dying man's bedside two farmhands, who were about harvest work in one of his fields near the cliff, heard a hollow voice, as if coming from the sea, which said, 'The hour is come but the man is not come.'

Looking in the direction whence the words came, they saw no person; but far out to sea they beheld a black, heavy, square-rigged ship, with all sail set, coming fast in, against wind and tide, and not a hand to be seen aboard her. She came so close under the cliff that only her topmast could be seen; then black clouds – that seemed to rise out of the deep – gathered around her and extended thence straight to the dying wrecker's dwelling.

The harvest men, terrified at the sight of this ship-of-doom so near them, ran up to the town-place just as the old sinner died, when his dwelling shook as if about to fall. Everybody rushed out and saw the black clouds roll off towards the death ship, which at once sailed away – amid a blaze of lightning – far over the sea, and disappeared.

The weather immediately cleared, and nothing unusual occurred until a few men assembled to put the wrecker's ghastly remains quickly off the face of the earth; then, as the coffin was borne towards the churchyard, a large black pig came – no one knew from whence – and followed the bearers, who all declared the coffin was too light to contain any body. The sky, too, became suddenly overcast and a tempest raged to that degree that they could scarcely keep on their legs to reach the churchyard stile, where such sheets of blinding lightning flashed around them that they dropped the coffin and rushed into the church.

The storm having abated, they ventured out, and found nothing of the coffin but its handles and a few nails, for it had been set on fire, and all else consumed, by the lightning.

The Cursing Psalm

Set thou a wicked man over him: and let Satan stand at his right hand.

There is a general belief, in the western part of Cornwall, that if a greatly injured person, the last thing before death, reads or recites the 109th Psalm, applying its comminations to the injurer, the dying maledictions are sure to take effect.

Nearly a hundred years ago there lived in Gwinear churchtown a young man called Thomas Thomas, who for many years courted his cousin, Elizabeth Thomas, of the same place. She was much attached to the young man, who often promised to make her his wife; but, when she had shown her utmost trust in him, on some little disagreement he slighted her and proposed to wed another damsel of the same village.

One Sunday afternoon he took his new love for a walk, passing by his old sweetheart's door, purposely to spite her.

Soon after they had passed her cottage, the betrayed and wronged girl, who was of a very hasty temper, took a rope and a prayer-book, went into a roadway field, and hanged herself near the path by which her faithless lover and his new fiancée had passed, and would, probably, return.

Thus it was that her former lover found her hanging from the tree, quite dead, with the prayer-book lying open by her feet. A leaf had been turned down to mark the place of the Cursing Psalm. On the page was written 'When this you see, remember me.' Thomas then knew that she had doomed him and for a long while wandered about like one distracted, working in various parts of the country, sometimes at mining, other times at husbandry, and never returned to Gwinear churchtown.

Little was seen of him, by anyone who knew him, until after some years, when he went to live in Market-jew (Marazion). He would never venture to church or chapel for fear of hearing read the 109th Psalm; he dreaded even to pass near a school for the same reason. He was several times hurt in the mines, and he attributed all his misfortunes and bad luck to the curse of Elizabeth, whose avenging ghost often appeared to him – as well by day as by night – with an open prayer-book in her hand.

Not withstanding the distraction of his mind, he was still a fine, strong, lusty man, and many of his comrades advised him to get married, saying that there was nothing like a living wife to drive away the spirit of a dead sweetheart. Taking their advice he paid his addresses to several young women of the neighbourhood and others further away; but they, one and all, flouted him with scorn, for the history of his unfortunate first love was blown far and near. If he persisted in his suit the indignant damsels would ask him with a sneer if he wished to bring all the ill-wishes of the 'Cursing Psalm' on their heads, too.

At length, however, a widow in Market-jew took pity on Thomas and consented to venture her lot with him; and Elizabeth's ghost ceased persecuting him, for a short while.

But on the road to St Hilary's Church – whither Thomas and the widow proceeded to get married – the weather suddenly changed; from calm and sunshine it became a tempest, with thunder and lightning. It was harvest time, and a cloud, black as night, hung over them, and rain poured down on the churchway path, while they saw people binding barley in the fields on either hand.

Thomas, trembling with fear, saw his sweetheart's ghost, with her open book, standing menacingly in the path before him, and he would have turned back had not the widow urged him on, saying that she saw no ghost, and did not mind her nor yet her book, and got him married. He lived for a few years pretty tranquilly, and his wife bore him two children. Then he was again disturbed with visits from the avenging ghost and some misfortune or sickness always closely followed its appearance, until Thomas – worn out in body and mind – when less than forty years of age died, and was buried in St Hilary's.

The Death of Admiral Sir Cloudesley Shovell

We are reminded by the above of the wreck of Admiral Sir Cloudesley Shovell's ship, the *Association*, at Scilly; and of a tradition, common to the Islands, which attributes that disaster to the reading or reciting of the 109th Psalm, shortly before death, by one of Sir Cloudesley's crew, whom he unjustly condemned to be hanged.

The Admiral was returning with his fleet from Toulon, when, on the evening of 22 October 1707, his ship struck on the Gilstone, about three and a half miles from St Agnes; and in a few minutes afterwards went down, and everybody on board perished, except one man, who saved himself by floating on a piece of timber to a rock called Hellweathers – about two and a half miles from the Gilstone – where

This coat of arms was salvaged from the wreck of the *Association* and is now in the Town Hall at Penzance.

he remained some days before the weather permitted any boat to approach and take him off to St Agnes.

He is said to have stated that the day before the Admiral's ship was wrecked, one of the crew, who was a native of Scilly and well acquainted with the channel, represented to Sir Cloudesley that the course the ship was taking would bring her on Scilly rocks. The Admiral and his officers were incensed at the man's interference; and because he persisted in affirming that the ship's way was wrong and would bring them to destruction, Sir Cloudesley Shovell – rather summarily, one might now think – condemned the man to be hanged for insubordination and endeavouring to excite a mutiny.

When the poor fellow was tied to the mast, preparatory to his being suspended by his neck from the yard-arm, he begged as a last favour that a Psalm might be read before his execution. His request being granted, he selected the 109th, and repeated certain imprecatory portions of it after the reader; and the last words he uttered were to the effect that Sir Cloudesley Shovell and those who saw him hanged should never reach the land alive.

His body, shrouded in a hammock, with a shot to sink it, was cast

Sir Cloudesley Shovell, 1650–1707 (National Portrait Gallery). 65

into the deep and but little heed paid to the dying sailor's final sentence. Shortly after, however, the sky, which had been gloomy all day, became much darker; black, lowering clouds hung over the fleet like a funeral pall, and the gale rose to a violent tempest. Then the hanged man's curse was dreaded; and lo, to the crew's consternation, they beheld his corpse – divested of its rude winding-sheet – floating near the doomed ship, which it closely followed, with its face turned towards her – in all her varying course, through eddying currents – until she struck on the Gilstone; when the hanged man went down with the ship and his messmates.

At this unfortunate time there perished, besides the Admiral, several officers, and about two thousand men, belonging to the *Association* and other vessels of the fleet.

Sir Cloudesley Shovell's body was washed ashore at Porth Hellick Bay, in St Mary's, about eight miles from the Gilstone. It was quite naked on the hatch of a ship on which he had endeavoured to save himself – and a little dog lay by him – when he was found by a soldier and his wife, who only knew him to be the Admiral by a diamond ring on his finger. They buried him in the sand, where a pit on Porth Hellick Bank still marks the grave. The pit never fills up in the greatest storms, and no grass ever grows on this blasted grave, though the ground around it is often green.

Connected with this unfortunate occurrence, there is a gratifying bit of true history – we cannot say so much for all the above – which says that Lady Shovell, on having her husband's ring by which his body was identified, gave the soldier who found it a pension for life. The Admiral was deposited in Westminster Abbey where his monument recalls the direful tale.

A Ghostly Ship's Bell

In the southern side of St Levan's churchyard there is a low altar-tomb on the grave of Captain Wetherel, whose ship sprung a leak and sank, and who was drowned near the Rundle Stone (Runnelstone) many years ago. This grave is regarded with fear and wonder by many persons of that neighbourhood; for ever since the captain was laid there, it has been believed that a ghostly bell strikes the hours and half-hours in his grave, the same as on board ship.

'Tis said this sound beneath the sod may be heard the clearest by persons passing the churchyard at midnight. It was a few minutes before that hour, when the captain, finding his vessel sinking, made his crew take to the boat. He himself refused to quit his ship, and, as she went down, they heard him give eight loud and distinct strokes on the bell.

Many years since several young people were assembled in the churchyard one Sunday forenoon after service had commenced and the elders had gone into church. Time passed pleasantly with the young folks in chatting about such occurrences of the St Levan world as interested them. In rambling among the graves, to look at the many garden flowers that bloomed on them, they approached Captain Wetherel's tomb, and a girl who stood by it reading the inscription started back on hearing a hollow sound beneath her feet. She, and others near her who saw her emotion, listened, and lo! a ringing came up as of a bell at sea; all rushed into church in great fright. There was much talk of the strange occurrence for a few weeks and less loitering of the youngsters to gossip in the churchyard during service.

Shortly after a young sailor, belonging to St Levan who had been absent for many years, came home for a few weeks; being in the Elder Tree public-house one forenoon with some of his former companions, their discourse led to the mention of the ship's bell sounding in Captain Wetherel's grave. The young seaman said he believed the story was all nonsense, though as strange or stranger things happened in old vessels; but, as it was then near upon twelve o'clock,

for curiosity sake, he went out and stood near the captain's tomb, while his comrades remained by the church porch, for a few minutes, watching the sundial. As it marked noon the sailor rushed back to his companions and, looking pale as a corpse, said with bated breath, 'True as I'm alive, I heard eight bells struck in the grave and wouldn't go near the spot again for the world.'

The young seaman on his next voyage found his grave in the deep.

I never heard of any other person who went purposely to hear the captain's bell, for it is a general belief here that bad luck is sure to overtake those who endeavour to pry into ghostly doings that do not concern them. Although the belief still holds, most West Country folks have become shy of mentioning Captain Wetherel's bell, or of talking of kindred subjects, except among ourselves, from the ridicule with which it is now fashionable to treat such matters, even in St Levan.

The Ghosts of Kenegie

Old folks of Gulval say that, in their grandparents' time, the ancient mansion of Kenegie and its grounds were constantly haunted by three 'sperats', and, on some nights, by many more.

The first ghost of whom there is any remembrance, and the one which remained longest, was the spirit of thrifty old Harris, who made great additions to the house and walled gardens, and was most unwilling to die and leave them. This spirit, however, gave but little trouble. He merely came on a certain night in every year – which was known to his descendants – to review the place in which he had taken so much delight; and only required that, on the night of his accustomed visit, the principal entrance door should be left open, as well as one opposite, opening into a paved court surrounded by offices.

At that time the grand entrance was approached by a straight, stately avenue, flanked by a bowling green, with a picturesque two-storeyed summer-house or 'look-out' at its further end. It was believed that any negligence in leaving open these doors at the stated time would be a cause of misfortune to the Harris family, or a token of its decline.

Consequently, this custom was duly observed from further back than there is any remembrance, until within a few years of the time when the last Harris of Kenegie disposed of his ancestral home. 'Tis said that when the spirit came and found the doors closed – through some mistake, it is supposed – he made much unearthly wailing, till cock-crowing, then went away moaning and never returned.

It is surmised that when the old family residence, in which he so much delighted, came into the possession of strangers, he neither desired to see it nor to hear of it again; and that he has, ever since, shut himself up in his family vault where he has plenty of company, as one may judge from the great number of monuments in Gulval Church, recording the virtues of his descendants. Before that unlucky time, crickets were heard chirruping around the hearths of

69

their old home all night long, but afterwards not one was heard or seen – sure token of impending misfortune.

The next ghostly visitor, and a more troublesome one, had been housekeeper and a great favourite with a later Squire Harris, much to the prejudice of his son and heir. The very night after her funeral disturbances began; the whole household was annoyed by this hussy of a ghost prancing along stone-paved passages, from one room to another – doors clashing and banging behind her – till she entered the kitchen, where she would next be heard winding up the great roasting-jack – one of the old-fashioned noisy clockwork machines.

After an interval of scolding, shrieking, and the other accessories of a row, she would beat the table or dresser-bed with a rolling-pin, and make the pewter plates rattle by way of announcing, as she was wont to do, that the roast was ready, and to summon the servants to dish it up. At length the inmates were glad to hear her high-heeled shoes patting over stairs and along the gallery, until they stopped at her late master's bedchamber door, which was usually the conclusion of her noisy exploits for the night.

The shadowy figure of this old woman, in a long-bodied gown and kirtle, was frequently seen passing quickly through the court. Now and then it happened that a new servant, wishing to get ahead with her work (on washing days especially) and not hearing any disturbance, ventured down in the small hours of the morning; but, on entering the kitchen, her light was almost always blown out, and she got a slap in the face from an invisible hand that made her see fire before her eyes; and, on turning to leave the room, received a kick behind which made her remember to stay abed till cock-crowing.

The housekeeper was put to rest, however, many years before the Harrises left their old home, and bound to perform such a task as she richly deserved. She was confined to a small room on the eastern or northern side of the house; with her were placed a fleece of black wool, a pair of cards, a distaff and spindle, and knitting needles. With these she was required to card the black fleece until it became white, and then to spin it and knit stockings of the yarn. Her closet door is walled up or plastered over so that few know exactly where it is situated, though old folks who served the Harris family say they have often heard the clicking of cards in some remote part of the building, and that there was always a little hole, such as sparrows might nest in, through the wall; if filled up it was sure to be opened over night without being touched by mortal hands.

The last Ghost of Kenegie – at least of whom there is any trustworthy tradition – was that of a spendthrift heir known as 'Wild Harris' who is best remembered because the power of ordinary clergymen was found insufficient to lay him. He extended his walks all over the grounds and far away down in the 'bottom' towards the mill. He was also seen on horseback chasing with one hound, on Kenegie downs and elsewhere. Belated market folks and others dreaded to pass Kenegie Gate, for they frequently saw the 'Squire's Sperat' standing in an alcove, just over this grand entrance. The ghost mostly wore a steeple-crown and feather, hunting-coat and riding-boots, or a long, black gown and flat cap, with lace and plume.

On winter nights the Squire's ghost, with a dozen or more of his old cronies or like spirits, would assemble in the bowling-green summer-house, where they might be seen and heard from the mansion even, talking, singing, swearing and shouting in a state of uproarious mirth. Altogether Kenegie must have been a lively place of nights, with the old housekeeper re-enacting scenes of her former rule within and Wild Harris's nocturnal carouse in the summer-house. Few servants, however, lived there long; they did not relish such ghostly merriment in which they had no other share than to be kept awake and terrified all night.

Wild Harris is said to have been an eager sportsman, with much wild-oats in his composition, who cared for little else but his hunter and hounds, except a young lady, a poor relation, dependent on his family with whom she lived much like a fish out of water, being regarded as too low for the parlour on grand occasions, and, at all times, as too low for the kitchen, where she was treated as an intruder by the crone-like housekeeper and her creatures.

This unfortunate damsel passed much of her time in the pleasant upper room of the summer-house with old maiden ladies of the family, who here wrought everlasting tapestry, fine lace, or embroidery.

When this poor gentlewoman was in her bloom, Wild Harris's father was a widower in his dotage, and too much influenced by his housekeeper, who during his wife's lifetime had been a special favourite with him. The old faggot, may she never cease carding and her wool never become white! She ever disliked her young master and detested the poor orphan lady, of whom she was jealous, fearing lest she might supplant her one day in governing the household. The dame was a malicious spy on the lovers, who frequently met in the summer-house and in secluded walks in the vale.

The old gentleman was much prejudiced against his poor cousin by being persuaded that, only for this unfortunate attachment, his son would have married a rich heiress, whose lands lay near the Harris' up-country property. He declared that the day his son married his cousin, he would wed his housekeeper, so that she would still rule the roost. In spite of all opposition, however, the young man would have made an 'honest woman' of his betrothed, but was hindered by the malice of the old dame and his father until too late; for the poor damsel, distracted with grief, wandered away one night and next morning was found by her lover drowned in a mill-pond.

Shortly after this tragic event the old Squire died, and Wild Harris found himself master of Kenegie, but disinherited of much other property. He had some satisfaction, however, in turning to doors the old mischief-making minion, but not much; she soon fretted herself to death, and was hardly laid in her grave ere she was back again, making such a din, out of mere spite, as hindered the inmates from getting a wink of sleep during the dead hours of night.

The master of Kenegie became more reckless than ever; his days were spent in hunting, his nights in revelry. He kept open house for rich or poor, who chose to partake of his hospitality. One and all were cordially welcomed. With all his faults, he had an open heart and hand; but, in a few years, he came to an untimely end, while still in his prime, by a fall from his horse when hunting on the Castle Downs. It is said that his horse was startled by a white hare that often followed him, and was thought to be the unfortunate lady's spirit.

He was borne to Gulval Church and laid in the vault at night, as was the fashion with some of our old families. His burial was attended by many friends, and when some of them – who remained late at the funeral supper – came down the avenue to return home, they beheld him, as natural, seemingly, as life, standing by the summer-house steps, arrayed in his hunting-dress, and, by his side, a favourite old dog that had died when his master had breathed his last.

Laying Wild Harris's Ghost

The housekeeper was confined to her task, as already stated, long before the family succeeded in getting Wild Harris laid. Many ineffectual attempts were made which only resulted in harm, by raising tempests which destroyed crops on land and life at sea; besides, after these vain trials of parsons' power the ghost became more troublesome for a while than he was before their interference with his walks.

Fortunately, however, the Reverend Mr Polkinghorne, of St Ives, acquired the virtue whereby he became the most powerful exorcist and spirit-queller west of Hayle.

From the little that is known of this gentleman one may infer that he was not by any means such as would now be styled a pious character. He is said to have been the boldest fox-hunter of these parts, but he would never chase a hare. He kept many of these creatures running about the house like cats; foolish people said they were the parson's familiar spirits, or witches he found wandering in that shape. The parson was mostly accompanied by his horse and dog which both followed him. When he stopped to chat, Hector, his horse, came up and rested his head on his master's shoulder, as if desirous of hearing the news too. If he called at a house both his attendants waited at the door, his horse never requiring to be held. He made long journeys with his steed walking alongside or behind him, the bridle-rein passed round its neck and the stirrups thrown across the saddle. Wonderful stories are also told about the high hedges and rocky ground that the parson's horse would take him safely over when after the hounds; and how the birds, which nested undisturbed in his garden, and other dumb creatures seemed to regard him as one of themselves.

On being requested to do his utmost in order that Wild Harris's ghost might rest in peace or be kept away from Kenegie, the reverend gentleman replied that he hoped to succeed if it were in the power of man to effect it. Other clergymen, hearing of what was about to be attempted, expressed a wish to be present at the proceedings. Mr Polkinghorne replied that he neither required their assistance nor desired their presence, yet, any of his reverend brethren might please themselves for what he cared. Moreover, he charged them that if they came to Kenegie on the appointed night, not to intermeddle in any way, whatever might happen.

A night in the latter end of harvest was chosen for this arduous undertaking. Several clergymen being anxious to see how the renowned spirit-queller would act with a ghost that had baffled so many of them, about an hour before midnight four from the westward of Penzance, a young curate of St Hilary's, and another from some parish over that way, arrived at Kenegie and waited a long while near the gate, expecting Mr Polkinghorne. At the turn of the night a terrific storm came on and the six parsons, drenched to their skins, took refuge in the summer-house. Candles had been lit in the upper room of this building as it was understood that the spirit-quelling operations would be performed there. They waited long, but neither Polkinghorne nor Harris's ghost appearing, the curate of St Hilary's – impatient of inaction – took from his breast a book and read there-from some conjuring formulas, by way of practice, or for mere pastime. As he read, a crashing thunder-clap burst over the building, shook it to its foundations, and broke open the window. The parsons fell on the floor, as if stunned, and on opening their eyes, after being almost blinded by lightning, they beheld near the open door a crowd of 'Bukka Dhu' (black spirits, imps perhaps) grinning at them, and then partially disappearing in a misty vapour, to be succeeded by others, who all made ugly faces and contemptuous or threatening gestures.

The reverend gentlemen crawled to the window and looked out, to avoid the sight of such ugly spectres and to get fresh air – that in the room smelt worse than the fumes of brimstone. Presently an icy shiver ran through them and they felt as if something awful had entered the room. On glancing round, they beheld the apparition of a man standing with his back to the fireplace and looking intently towards the opposite wall. His eyes never winked or turned away, but seemed to gaze on something beyond the blank wall. He wore a long black gown or loose coat which reached the floor; his face appeared sad and wan, under a sable cap, garnished with a plume and lace. He seemed unconscious of either the black spirits' or the parsons' presence. Over a while he turned slowly round, advanced towards the window with a frowning countenance which showed the parsons that he regarded them as intruders; and they, poor men, trembling in every limb and with hair on end, pressed each other into the open window intending to drop themselves to the ground and risk broken bones or concussion, for they were most of them fat and heavy.

Meanwhile scores of 'Bukkas' continued to hover behind the ghost, grimacing as if they enjoyed the parsons' distress. Every minute seemed an hour to the terrified gentlemen; but, just as some of them got their legs out of the casement, the tread of heavy boots was heard on the stone stairs and Polkinghorne bounced into the room, whereupon the ghost, turning quickly round, exclaimed, 'Now Polkinghorne, that thou art come, I must be gone!' The conjurer holding out his hand towards the spirit, said quietly '*In nomine Domini*, I bid thee stay'; then he turned to the black spirits, made a crack with his hunting whip, and said, 'Avaunt, ye Bukka Dhu', and off they went, at his word, howling and shrieking louder than the tempest. The ghost stood still; Polkinghorne uttered long words in an unknown tongue while he drew around it, on the sanded floor with his whip-stick, a circle and magical signs, with a five-pointed star (pentagram) to lock the circle. He continued speaking a long while without pausing, and his words sounded deep and full, as if, at once, near and far off, like the surging of billows on a long stretch of shore, or thunder echoing around the hills.

At length the spirit felt the able conjurer's power and crouched down at his feet, holding out his hands as if praying him to desist. Mr Polkinghorne, while still saying powerful words, unwound a few yards of new hempen cord from around his waist, leaving much more of it attached. Having made a loop at the end he passed it over the ghost's head and under his arms; then, addressing him, said, '*In nomine Domini*, I bid thee stand up and come with me.' On saying this he lifted the spirit's skirts up from the floor with his whip-stick, and under them nothing was seen but flaming fire.

Now he had the spirit standing beside him, with his eyes fixed and his limbs motionless like one spellbound, he exclaimed, 'Thank the Powers, it's all right so far.' Casting a glance towards the other parsons, and seeing a book on the floor, he took it up, opened it, and speaking for the first time to his reverend brethren, said, 'You, too, may thank your lucky stars I came in the nick of time to save you from grievous harm.' Holding the book towards the curate from St Hilary, he continued, 'This belongs to you, my weak brother; strange such a book should be in your possession! The penmanship is beautiful, it must have cost a mint of money, yet it is worse than useless – nay, it's perilous to such as you. By good luck you read what merely brought hither silly Bukkas, but if you had chanced to pronounce a word on the next leaf that you cannot understand, you would have called forth such malignant fiends, flying in the tempest this awful night, as would have torn you limb from limb, or have carried ye away bodily. Perhaps, becoming tired, they might have fixed ye on St Hilary steeple. For my part I wish you were there lest a greater evil befall thee this night.'

Saying that, he cast down the book; spoke a few words which the others didn't understand; drew his foot over a magic sign that locked the charmed circle, and, turning towards the spirit, said, '*In nomine Domini*, come thou with me', and Wild Harris's ghost was led away, quiet as a lamb.

Mr Polkinghorne, having reached the outer gate, took his horse which he had left there. The poor beast trembled even though this ghost was not the first, by many, that it had been near. Having mounted he gave the ghost more rope and bade him keep further from Hector. A minute afterwards the four West Country parsons took downhill as fast as their horses could lay feet to ground.

Few bleaker places are to be found than the old road to St Ives, passing over Kenegie downs. When they got there the wind seemed to beat on them from all points at once; rain and thunder never ceased; the Castle-hill seemed all ablaze with lightning; at times, too, when a more violent blast than usual whirled round them clouds of fiends hovered overhead like foul birds of prey. The sky was pitch black, and demons were only seen by the forked lightning that burst from their midst. The ghost, as if seeking protection, came nearer the parson; then his horse's terror became painful to witness, until a few magical words and a crack of his whip sent the devils howling away, and the ghost to the end of his rope. At last they came within a stone's cast of a few dwellings called Castle-gate, and leaving the highway took a path on the left that wound up the hill to Castle-an-dinas.

The parson's Hector was well acquainted with the lay of the country all around as he had often crossed it following the hounds, and, after scrambling through the narrow lane, tried his utmost to take away down the moorland to a smith's shop in Hellangove where he had often been shod. By a firm hand on the bridle-rein his master kept him uphill for a furlong or so, when they came to an old gurgie

(hedge of stone) that once enclosed a fold. On one side of this was a bowjey (cattle or sheep-house). Mr Polkinghorne alighted, turned his horse into the derelict shelter, and bade the ghost follow him.

They walked on in silence until they came to the castle's outer enclosure, which screened them from the blast. Then the reverend gentleman said, 'Now that we are alone, and not likely to suffer any more intrusion, tell me, my unhappy brother, what it is that disturbs thy rest? Be assured, my desire is to procure thee peace.'

The spirit replied to the effect that, at the time of his decease, he was much troubled, because he owed several sums to workpeople and others, fearing they would not be paid by his successor. Moreover, he related how he had walked about for years, hoping some honest body would speak to him; how the longer he was left unspoken to the more uneasy and troublesome he became; and when his relations brought the parsons to lay him, who were unqualified for that office, he was much exasperated, and he determined never to leave Kenegie. Finally, there were other failings which lay heavy on his conscience and which he could confess only to a man of God.

The poor ghost having unburthened himself, Mr Polkinghorne gave him words of comfort, promised to see that his debts would be paid, and concluded by saying, 'Think no more about your little faults and failings, for if, when in mortal life, you had more of what we call the devil in ye, you would have overcome your opponents, and much grief would have been spared to yourself and others.'

Then the parson took the cord off, saying, 'This is no longer required to protect ye from evil spirits, for they have all departed with the tempest they raised and the sky is now serene.'

As they ascended the hill the moon shone bright on the old fort's inner enclosing wall, which was then almost intact. The upper enclosure is nearly oval in outline, and they entered it at its south-eastern end. Stopping a minute on the hill-top, Mr Polkinghorne said to the ghost, 'There is no cure for a troubled spirit equal to constant employment, and I shall allot you an easy task, which, with time and patience, will procure ye repose; but I must first make the whole of this enclosure secure against infernal spirits.'

Having placed the ghost on his right-hand side, he passed with him three times around the enclosed hill-top, going from east to west, or with the sun, and keeping close to the wall. At the first round, he merely counted the number of paces; at the next, he uttered, in some ancient Eastern tongue, such exorcisms and adjurations as serve to expel infernal spirits; at the last circuit he made twelve mystic signs at equal distances near the bounding wall. He then passed through the middle of the ground to its north-western end, cutting the air with his whip, and tracing on the earth more magical figures. Being arrived at the end opposite the entrance, he drew a line with his whip-stick from a large stone in the wall on one side, to another opposite, and told the spirit to remember them as bound-stones. The space thus marked off might be three or four 'laces' of pretty even grass-covered ground, with a few furze bushes and large stones scattered over it.

The reverend gentleman rested a while on the ruined wall, which rose some ten feet above a surrounding foss, and three or four from the inner ground.

'Now, my son,' said he, turning towards the ghost who stood near, 'all within the castle's upper walls is as safe for ye as consecrated ground; and here is your task, which is merely to count the blades of grass on this small space, bounded by the wall and a straight line from stone to stone, that you can always renew or find.

'You must reckon them nine times, to be sure that you have counted right; you need not set about it till I leave, there's plenty of time before ye. While at your work banish from your thoughts all remembrance of past griefs by thinking of pleasant subjects. There is nothing better for this purpose than the recollection of such old world stories as delighted our innocent childhood, and please us in mature age.'

The spirit looked disconcerted and said that he thought the assigned task a vain one, as it produced nothing of lasting use. He would rather be employed in repairing the castle walls, or some such job.

'No, my dear son,' replied the parson, 'it would never do for ye to be employed on anything that would be visible to human eyes. The unusual occurrence would draw hither such crowds of gazers as would greatly incommode ye. No more need ye trouble yourself on the score of its mere use, in your sense; for if restless mortals employed themselves solely in such works of utility as you mean, the greater part of them would find nothing to do, and be more miserable than ghosts unlaid. Indeed, except honest husbandmen, simple artisans, and a few others, the rest might just as well pass their time in spinning ropes of sand, counting blades of grass, or in any other ghostly employment, for all the good they do, unless it be to tranquillise their restless minds.'

The ghost made no reply, but seemed all down in the mouth, which expression of sadness the parson remarked, and said, 'Don't ye be out of heart, brother, but have patience, and you will find that years will pass away like a summer's day. Then you will wonder how your mortal crosses ever had the power to trouble ye. All remembrance of them will fade like a dream, and you will rest in peace. When you have mind to pause awhile – say after each time of counting – you can go

around the hill-top and enjoy the extensive prospect, as all within this higher rampart is a charmed circle for ye, where fiends dare not enter. There are other pleasant sights which you will often behold; for the small people still keep to the Castle-hill and hold their dances and fairs, of summer nights, within these ramparts. But now, it's high time for you to become invisible and for me to leave ye. The cocks will soon be crowing; see how fast the light increases on Carn Brea and other noble hills that were the giants' dwelling places in days of yore and stand out against the grey sky like sentinels over this favoured Western Land.'

The parson, pointing to the eastern sky, told the spirit to put off his form. In a minute or so the apparition became indistinct, and faded gradually away, like a thin wreath of smoke dissolving in air.

Mr Polkinghorne said farewell, and as he turned to leave the spirit to his task he heard a hollow voice say, 'Good friend, do thou remember me, and visit me again.'

When the reverend gentleman entered the old bowjey the joy that his horse showed at his approach was like recalling him from death to life. As he slowly wended his way homeward, Mr Polkinghorne was grieved to see the wreck made by the preceding night's tempest. In Nancledra, low lying as it is, dwellings were unroofed and trees, which had withstood the storms of centuries, were all uprooted. On higher ground stones were blown out of hedges, arish mows laid low, and the corn whirled around fields.

About sunrise, St Ives folks, standing at their doors, were surprised to see their beloved parson coming down the Stennack, looking so sad and weary that he did not even give them 'the time of day' with his accustomed cheerful tone and pleasant smile. Neither he or his steed were again seen in the street for several days after their ghostly night's work.

The Seaman's Ghost of Zennor

James Bottrell, one of the St Just family of that name, after having served many years aboard a privateer when he was a young man in Bonaparte's time, settled in Zennor, about fifty years ago. Shortly after he left sea he was much troubled with a drowned shipmate's ghost. Towards the morning part of a stormy winter's night he was aroused by three loud raps on his chamber window. On raising his head he saw standing by his bedside the apparition of one John Jones, who had been his favourite comrade, looking pale and sad, and, apparently, dripping wet. In a few minutes it disappeared with the misty light which surrounded it.

Next day James tried to persuade himself that the vision might be merely a troubled dream, but the apparition continued to come on each succeeding night, stopping longer than at first. There was also much noise and disturbance in and around his dwelling, by day as well as by night.

Over a week or so the ghost, often casting an angry look at the man, followed him about in broad daylight, so that James became weary of his life. His friends advised him to speak to the ghost and have confidence, as they had always been good friends; they told him that a spirit would never speak until spoken to, believing that his shipmate merely wanted him to do something that the ghost was unable to perform. Moreover, they warned him that there was danger to be apprehended when a spirit was angered by delay in speaking to it.

At length James plucked up courage, and one day, being at work in a field, when his old mate's ghost stood by him – as usual looking sad and angry by turns – he spoke, and said, 'Tell me, John Jones, what shall I do to give thee rest?' The spirit replied, 'It is well thou hast spoken, for I should have been the death of thee if thou hadst much longer refused to speak! What grieved and vexed me most was to see that thou seemedst to fear thy old comrade, who always liked thee the best of all his shipmates.'

'I no longer fear thee, Jack,' replied James, 'and wish I could grasp

81

that hand of thine as in times gone by.'

The spirit, looking pleased, said, 'Now I see thee art like thyself again, staunch and true to thy comrade in life and death. Listen and learn why I am come to seek thy aid. The other stormy night, a few minutes before I first appeared at thy bedside, I was on board a good ship in the Bay of Biscay, with a strong gale and a rolling sea. In clewing up a topsail, the ship gave a lurch: I lost my hold, fell overboard, and was drowned before anyone noticed my mishap. When sinking I thought of thee. Now much of my prize-money is in a chest, left in Plymouth in a public-house well known to thee – the one we used most frequent, when everything was in common between us. My son, I want thee to go thither; take my chest to another house; pay what I owe to various people in Plymouth, and keep what remains for thyself. I'll meet thee there and direct thee how to act.'

Early next morning James took a strong young horse and rode away to Plymouth. It was after candlelighting of the second night when he arrived there, and put up at an inn a short distance from the one where the chest was left.

While he lay awake, thinking how he should proceed on the morrow, Jones appeared by his bedside, and, as if knowing what passed in the man's mind, said, 'Don't 'e think, my son, that the landlady will make any difficulty about taking away the chest, for she don't know, d'ye see, that it contains valuables, nor that I shipped aboard an Indiaman and got drowned a few weeks ago. But she remembers how – not long since – we wore each other's clothes and shared our rhino, just as brothers should. Tell her I'm in town and will see her before I leave! Tomorrow bring here the chest and I'll direct 'e how to deal with my creditors; and now good night, mate.' Saying this he vanished.

The landlady was very glad to see James, and more so to have the sailor's chest taken out of her way. She told him to give her love to Captain Jones (as she called him) and to say that she hoped he would not fail to call before he left port. The chest being opened, there was nothing to be seen in it but the seaman's best clothing, for all the money was concealed in secret drawers of the skibbet, and under a false bottom. The ghost accompanied James – though invisible to others – all the time, until the business was settled. Then it left him – without saying good-bye, however.

James went over to Dock. While he was there admiring the shipping, on turning around he saw Jones close beside him. If he had been visible to other people he would have been taken as an able seaman in his prime, for he appeared rigged out in brand-new sailor's garb and looked as hale and hearty as when alive. 'I've just passed by the old inn,' said he, 'showed myself as I now appear, and kissed my hand to our old hostess, who was at her work near an open window; but, before she could reach her door to welcome home the man she used to admire, lo! I'm here. So you see it's convenient to be a ghost!'

James did not think so, however; and they walked on in silence till they came near a fine ship ready to sail on a long voyage. Then the spirit stopped, and, looking sorrowfully in the man's face, said, 'My dear Jim, I will now bid thee farewell. I'm off to sea again, for, with an occasional trip to the Green, I know no way of passing the time that better suits me. Thou wilt nevermore see me while thou art alive, but if thou thinkest of me at the hour of thy death we shall meet, as soon as the breath leaves thy body. My poor clay lies deep in the Bay of Biscay, and when thine is laid in Zennor churchyard we will rove the sea together. A truehearted tar has nothing to fear, and now my son adieu.' A moment after, James saw him glide aboard the ship, and in the twinkling of an eye he vanished.

James returned to the inn, feeling very wisht, and his sadness continued till he came in sight of Zennor Hills. Then he felt in pretty good heart, and well he might, for had he not brought home a bundle of capital clothes that he found in his comrade's chest and many more pounds in his pocket than when he left Zennor? But the horse was never fit for anything again, from having been ridden to and from Plymouth in less than a week.

Sailors say that ships are often haunted with drowned seamen's ghosts, and they believe that such vessels are seldom wrecked, for the friendly spirits give warning of approaching tempests and tokens of other dangers to their craft.

Ghosts of Penzance

Little more than fifty years ago, the building in Chapel Street which now (1867) serves as a dispensary, with the adjoining house at the entrance to Vounderveor-lane, formed a mansion which belonged to an elderly lady, Mrs Baines. At that time there was in the rear of this mansion a large garden and orchard extending westward nearly to New Road, and bounded on the south by Vounderveor. The south side of the lane was an open field, and at its west end there were no dwellings.

Where the School of Art, the Methodist vestries, and other houses stand, was all known as Mrs Baines's orchard. This pleasant spot, in which the lady took great delight, was stocked with the choicest apple, pear, plum and other fruit trees then known. The town boys soon found out the fine flavour of Mrs Baines's fruit, which was to them all the sweeter for being stolen. When the apples were ripe and most tempting, the mistress and her serving-man watched the garden by turns – the man during the first part of the night, and madam would descend in her nightdress, every now and then, to see that all was right, in the small hours of morning.

One night Mrs Baines, suspecting that her man John was rather careless in keeping guard, sallied forth to see if he was attending to his duty, and, not finding him anywhere about the garden, she went to a tree of highly prized apples and shook down a good quantity, intending to take them away and thus prove to John that, through his remissness, the fruit was stolen. But her man was at no great distance, armed with an old blunderbuss charged with peas and small shot, dozing beneath a hedge. The rustling of shaken branches and noise of falling apples awoke him, and seeing somebody stealing apples from their favourite tree, he up with his gun and let fly at his mistress, exclaiming, at the same time, 'Now you thief, I've paid 'e off for keeping me out of bed to watch 'e! I know 'e, I do, and will bring 'e before his worship the mayor tomorrow!' 'Lord help me, I'm killed!' cried the lady as she fell on the ground. John stayed to see no more,

but, frightened out of his wits, ran away and could not be found for
several days. At last he was found up in Castle-an-dinas, half starved.
By good luck the old lady's back was towards her man when he fired,
and the greatest part of the charge took effect below her waist. Doctor
Giddy was fetched, and, after some delicate surgical operations
which the lady bore with exemplary patience, pronounced her fright
to be more than the hurt.

However, a short time after the old lady got shot, she died, and then
she kept such ward and watch over her orchard that few were so bold
as to enter into the haunted ground after day-down. Her ghost was
often seen under the tree where she was shot, or walking the garden.
Everybody knew the old lady by her upturned and powdered grey hair
under a lace cap of antique pattern; by the long lace ruffles hanging
from her elbows; her short silk mantle, gold-headed cane, and other
trappings of old-fashioned pomp.

There are many still living in Penzance who remember the time
when they would not venture on any account to pass through
Vounderveor-lane after nightfall for fear of Mrs Baines's ghost.
Sometimes she would flutter up from the garden or yard just like an
old hen and perch herself on the wall: then, for an instant, one might
get a glance of her spindle legs and high-heeled shoes before she
vanished.

Her walking in the garden might have been put up with, but she
soon haunted all parts of the premises and was often seen where

least expected both by night and at noon. The ghost became so troublesome, at last, that no person could be found to occupy the house, where she was all night long tramping about from room to room, slamming the doors, rattling the furniture and often making a fearful crash among glass and crockery. Even when there was no living occupant in the house, people standing in Chapel Street often saw a shadowy form through the windows, and lights glimmering in the parlours and bedrooms.

The proprietors, driven to their wits' end, unwilling that such valuable property should become worse than useless all through the freaks of this vexatious ghost, at last sent for a parson, who was much famed in this neighbourhood as an exorcist (we think the name of this reverend ghost layer was Singleton) that he might remove and lay the unresting spirit. He succeeded in getting her away down to the sandbanks on the Western Green, which were then spread over many acres of land where the waves now roll. Here this powerful parson, single-handed, bound her to spin from the banks ropes of sand for the term of a thousand years, unless she, before that time, spun a sufficiently long and strong one to reach from St Michael's Mount to St Clement's Isle. The encroaching sea having swept away the sandbanks, Mrs Baines's ghost is probably gone with them, as she has not been heard of for some years.

About the time Mrs Baines's ghost carried on its freaks in the mansion, an open pathway passed through St Mary's chapel-yard,

which was then often crossed, as it shortened the distance to the Quay. But for a long time few persons liked to pass through the burial-ground by night because a ghostly apparition, arrayed in white, was often seen wandering among the tombs, from which doleful sounds were frequently heard. Sometimes the fearful figure was also met on the path or seen in the chapel porch. One dark and rainy night, however, a sailor, who neither knew nor cared anything about the ghost of St Mary's, in taking the short cut through the chapel-yard, came as far as the chapel porch, when the ghost issued forth on the path and there stood, bobbing its head and waving its shroudings before him.

'Halloa! Who or what are you?' said the sailor.

'I am one of the dead!' the ghost answered.

'If you are one of the dead, what the deuce do you do here above ground? Go along down below!' said the sailor, as he lifted his fist and dealt the ghost a stunning blow over its head, which laid it sprawling on the stones, where it remained some time, unable to rise or descend, until a person passing by assisted it to its legs, and discovered the frolicksome gentleman, called Captain Carthew, who then lived in the house that is now Mrs Davy's property, and had long been diverting himself by personating the ghost, thus frightening the townsfolk out of their wits. The ghost was most effectually laid by Jack Tar, and served out for its tricks on the timid and credulous.

Sarah Polgrain

There are many stories connected with the old superstition that when rash lovers make vows to be constant to each other, 'living or dead', and one of the pledged dies far away from the other, the freed spirit traverses sea and land to fetch its affianced home to the land of shadows: the legend of the lovers of Porthgwarra told previously is founded on the same notion.

The most recent story we know (in which the same belief is shown to be still current) is that of Sarah Polgrain and Yorkshire Jack. The woman, who lived in Ludgvan within the present century, was hanged for poisoning her husband, that she might make room for a horse-dealer known as Yorkshire Jack. 'Tis said that the latter was much enamoured of the woman, and that they had been for a long time criminally acquainted before he succeeded in instigating her to commit the diabolical deed. Jack accompanied the woman on to the scaffold, and there, standing by the beam from which the murderess was in a few minutes to be launched into eternity, the unholy pair kissed each other; and promises, confirmed by oaths, passed between them the moment before the woman was executed. 'Tis said that Jack vowed to be with her in three years. Soon after the woman's execution Yorkshire Jack went to sea, that a roving life might dispel the gloomy thoughts caused by the remembrance of the reckless vow carelessly made to satisfy the dying woman.

Disasters constantly followed all the ships in which this unhappy wretch sailed. Three years from the hour of the woman's death Jack was on board a timber ship returning from Quebec when, about midway across the Atlantic, it was surrounded by a violent storm; the affrighted crew saw in the lurid thunder-clouds the figure of a fiery female form and another of gigantic size, too dreadful to look at! The figures stood over the ship when the crest of a mountain wave broke on the stern and swept the doomed man, who was then at the wheel, into the ocean. Immediately afterwards Yorkshire Jack was seen flying away to the westward between the figures who came in the

storm. These were no other than Sarah Polgrain and the evil spirit whose slave she had been on earth, and who was now her eternal master.

From the time that this western Jonah was taken away by the lady of his love and the devil, the ship was free from all the strange disasters which were constantly occurring on board during all the time that the haunted man was one of the crew.

This story obtained much notoriety from the anxiety of Ludgvan folks to prove that Sarah Polgrain had never been baptised in the water of their renowned saint's well, which is believed to protect all children baptised therein against the hangman and his hempen cord. Their joy was unbounded when it was found a mistake had been made about the woman's birthplace, and that she had been christened in a neighbouring parish, so that the wonderful character of the parish well obtained more widespread celebrity than ever, which it retains to this day.

The Keigwins of Mousehole

Half-an-hour's pleasant walk (from Newlyn) beside the seashore takes us to Mousehole. Near the middle of this interesting old town we pass over the bubbling brook which gave to this place its ancient and proper name of Moeshayle (young woman's brook), which has been Saxonised or corrupted into the unmeaning nickname of Mousehole.

A noteworthy object is the picturesque old mansion of the Keigwins, now transformed into a public-house. No wonder for these old gentry to be uneasy in their graves (as Mousehole people all know they are) to find their old mansion so degraded. Any person in the town will tell you there is scarcely a night but, at the usual hour for ghosts to leave their graves, these unresting old gentry revisit their family home and there hold a revel-rout for the best part of the night. There is such a noisy getting up and down stairs with the ghostly gentlemen's boots creaking and stamping, spurs and swords jingling, ladies' silks rustling and their hoops striking the banisters, that the living inmates get but little rest before cock-crow, when they betake themselves off. Sometimes these unwelcome visitors vary their fun by knocking about the furniture, smashing the glasses, having a dance, etc.: altogether they seem to be a right merry set of ghosts, yet they often succeed in making the tenants quit the house, as few persons like to have their sleep disturbed by such troublesome visitors.

The demeanour of the spirits of these old Keigwins is altogether different from that of well-behaved, serious, Christian ghosts; indeed they have at particular times made so much disturbance that no person in the house could get a wink of sleep, and, that they might be sent off if only for a time, the living inmates have had recourse to preachers and other pious folks; and they say that by their singing, praying, and other religious exercises, they have sometimes succeeded in driving these uneasy spirits from the house for a time.

One night, not long ago, the mistress of the house heard a noise in the large parlour, as if the chairs and tables were having a dance as well as the ghosts. This was followed by such a crash of breaking glass as if all the contents of the corner-buffet were dashed on the floor. The fear that all her beautiful old china and glass were gone to smash drove away all other dread, and the mistress ventured down, candle in hand, to see what was going on; but, when she ventured into the room, she saw the furniture was exactly as she had left it when she went to bed. The curious glasses, with twisted stems, and china punchbowls, were all safe and sound in the buffet. Believing then that there was no one but herself in the lower part of the house, she was proceeding to go upstairs, when, happening to cast a glance towards the broad landing, she saw a number of gentlemen and ladies ascending the stairs in great state – the ladies decked out in all the pride of hoops and farthingales, the gentlemen in laced coats, swords, and funnel-topped boots, with their rattling spurs: in fact, they were all equipped as they appeared in their old pictures, which were to be seen in some rooms of the ancient mansion a few years ago.

It is to be hoped that the old building will long be allowed to remain just as it is, without any further attempts to modernise it, as it is now the only good example we have near Penzance of the old mansion-house of the fifteenth century. Besides, the Keigwins of the Balcony House (as it is generally called) were persons of note in their day as soldiers and scholars. They are also intimately connected with the

romantic Spanish episode in the history of the place (1595). One of them, Jenkin Keigwin, distinguished himself at that time as a patriot. When defending the town against the invading Spanish he levelled at, and brought down with his musket, two of the enemy, but shortly after fell a victim to their overpowering force.

The good people of Mousehole have a firm belief in the wandering spirits who are supposed to inhabit a mid-region, and who are often permitted to occupy themselves with the same objects and pursuits as formerly constituted their business or their pleasure. The faith of the people respecting these visitors from the world of shadows is often confirmed by their favourite teachers from the pulpit.

A very intelligent woman of the place informed us that she heard a preacher, in the midst of his sermon on the invisible world, relate how, one Sunday night after the service at a country chapel, he went to visit a solitary cottage situated on a lonely moor. The footpath across the moor was scarcely visible in the darkening twilight; consequently he confined his regards to the ground near him, the best part of the way, so that he might keep on the path. A little before he reached the dwelling, looking towards it he saw three persons who

93

appeared to be females, dressed in white, a few yards before him, and proceeding towards the house. The preacher quickened his pace, as he wished to overtake them; yet, whether he walked fast or slow, the white figures always kept the same distance ahead. He noticed that they entered the small court before the cottage, but without the door being opened they disappeared, although there was no other outlet from the curtilage except the gate, which he was sure they did not re-pass. This surprised him, and it was then impressed on his mind that the apparition was that of visitors from the other world. When he entered the cottage (which he did by lifting the latch without knocking) he saw an aged woman seated on the chimney-stool in the large fireplace, such as we find in the country, where the fuel is furze and turf. After saluting the old woman, he enquired if any other persons had entered the cottage just before him. The old person replied that they were the only living persons in the house, but that her daughter was lying dead on a bed in the next room. When the preacher related to her what he saw, the old lady said that she understood very well what the vision was which he beheld: it was that of the spirits of the rest of the family, who had last died, come down to take the soul of her daughter away with them. The reverend gentleman told his congregation that he felt that the aged mother was right – in fact, he had not the least doubt about the correctness of what she felt, having known many similar instances of the kind himself.

Whether this story by the preacher to his congregation was that of a real apparition or mere fancy, the pleasing faith of the old lady was not the less consoling; nay, if the profane will say it is all imagination or whims, or apply the word 'superstition', it still contains one of those amiable and instinctive feelings dear to the heart of the bereaved.

The Cornish Giants

The Slaying of Old Denbras

A multitude of giants lived in Cornwall in the old days. The people then, it is said, were of much greater stature, commonly twice the size of men today. These were the descendants of the old masters of the world, the true Celts, who exceeded all other peoples in health and in the strength of their bodies, though paradoxically many modern pure-bred Cornishmen are of below-average height.

However, among these tall, strong people there lived a few who were giants indeed! One of them was Old Denbras of Towednack who built his castle across the main road that led from Market-jew (the old name for Marazion) to St Ives. He was in truth a giant among men, standing fifteen feet tall in his boots, with a girth more than proportionate to his height 'because he was very big-bellied, the effect of his gormandising, old age, and idle life'. His features were as terrifying as his size, with a thatch of unruly hair that had weathered to resemble a windswept brake of heather and teeth that were worn down to the gums, due to his diet of raw goats which he ate with their skins on, grinding down their bones with the remains of his teeth. Few ventured near his lands as he also had a reputation of eating his enemies. However, there were always some people, strangers to the district, innocent of the giant's existence.

One of these was a young lad named Tom. Tiring of his mother's endless tirade against his idleness he eventually left home and came at last to Market-jew where he decided to take a job. He was fortunate in that the first enquiry he made brought about employment. The mayor of the town was also its brewer, and perceiving that Tom was as honest as he was strong (he seems to have been of an average size for those days, being no more than eight feet tall though he was a good four feet across the shoulders) hired him to take a cartload of beer to St Ives. All went well with his journey for a time. He paused near Crowlas to help a dozen or so men who were attempting to load a huge tree-trunk on to a dray. They intended it to be one of the main timbers of a church that they were building. Seeing their difficulties

Tom told them to stand back and then lifted the great trunk on to the wagon himself without any sign of strain.

Not many miles further on he found his way blocked by the towering walls of a castle that had been erected across the highway. The walls were of such a height that they could only have been built by a giant, and it galled Tom that anyone, even a fierce giant, should act in such a selfish way. 'Well,' he said to himself, 'I don't see what right the old villain of a giant has got to build his hedges across the king's highway, and to enclose the common lands, any more than I or anybody else: the road belongs to go straight through here where he has placed his gate. They say he is a monstrous strong fellow; well, so am I, and which is the best man we will soon try. He waent eat me I s'pose. My old mammy never told me I should come by my death that way at all. I be cuss'd if I don't break down his gates and drive right through.'

Which is just what Tom did, and it was the resulting mayhem of splintering wood, falling timbers, and the hysterical barking of the resident dogs that awoke the giant abruptly from his after-lunch nap.

'Hallo!' says the giant. 'Who are you, you little scrub, to have the impudence to drive in here and disturb my nap. Es the beer for me? I didn't expect any.'

'You are heartily welcome to a drink,' Tom replied, 'but I am on my way to St Ives and will keep upon the old road, and the right road too, in spite of you and a better man than you.'

This answer annoyed the giant who began a ponderous descent from his castle, plucking a young elm tree (about twenty feet in height) on his way down and stripping branches and twigs from it so that it might better be used as a club. Meanwhile, Tom was busy taking the axle-tree off his cart. He left one wheel on so that it might be used as a shield against Denbras's elm tree.

However, Denbras was old and shaky. His great mowing sweeps with the tree were easily avoided by the agile Tom, who kept him at a distance with shrewd thrusts of the axle-tree. These sometimes caught the old giant off balance so that he fell to the floor. When this happened Tom would courteously help him back to his feet, give him a drink of ale, and hand back his tree-trunk club. Then hostilities would resume. This continued for a considerable time, so to bring a harmless conclusion to the conflict Tom reversed his weapon and gave a gentle thrust to the middle of his adversary's great pot belly. Really he meant no harm in this, never expecting the mortal effects that resulted. The end of the axle passed right through Denbras and as he fell (with a crash that was heard for miles around) he was pinned by it to the ground.

Tom was horror-struck to see what he had done to the poor giant and hurried to pull the weapon from his body; when he did so the blood ran down the hillside like a millstream and the agonised roars of Denbras echoed like thunder. Tom used great turves to stop the bleeding from the enormous wounds and held a barrel against the wounded ogre's lips in an attempt to revive him.

At length he stirred feebly and then spoke:

'It's all of no use, my son, I feel that I shall kick the bucket soon; I'm going round land fast, yet no man can but say that I died in fair fight, and I like thee better, for the sake of thy fair play, than any other man I ever fought with in all my born days. Thou art a true Cornish boy; I love thee like a brother: I have no near relations, and will make thee my son and heir; all my lands and treasure I give to thee. Now my breath is getting short, bow down thy ear my son, that thou mayest hear my dying wishes. Down in the caves of the castle there are lots of tin, gold, silver and other treasures. Mind the names of the dogs that watch the entrance, but tell to nobody else: they are called Standby and Holdfast. All my lands, for miles away to the north, all the hills between this and the sea, are stocked with oxen, deer, sheep, goats and other beasts, more than one can count – all rolling in fat, and all I give to thee, my son; only bury me decent, under a barrow, and don't let anyone abuse me after I'm gone. Be kind to the dogs, for my sake; and the tame cattle, poor things, I'm as sorry to leave them as if I'd been their father.'

Tom saw that the poor old fellow was sinking fast and so hurried to ask one last question of him:

'Oh, my dear daddy, don't go yet; stop a minute or two longer, and tell me what in the world I am to do with your wives? You haven't eaten them all, have 'ee? They say, down in the low countries, that they suppose that you have settled them that way; because, if what they say is true, you have enticed scores into your castle, and none ever came out again.'

At this the dying giant stirred angrily and replied, 'Oh! the wretches; may the devil fetch them for their slanderous tongues. I hoped to die in peace with all the world. Now listen to the truth, my son. The women know better, whatever they may say. Long before my first old woman was dead, they were always beating round my castle to see if I would take home another. All the stones I slung from the top of the hill would not make them stay away. The little, sickly, pale-faced women were the most troublesome of all. No use for me to tell each one who came to the gate that she was of a most unsuitable make for a giant's wife, and too weak to stand the wear and tear of a rough hill-country life. They would take no denial. The consequence was that in a short time they all died, as one may say, a natural death, and all of them blessed me with their latest breath. Under the barrows all around us, I have buried my dearest. On the sunny hill they rest, deck'd out and dress'd, and in their richest and rarest. What more could one do for them?'

The violent anger generated by the mention of this slander proved too much for Denbras, and he bowed his head and died, smiling yet resigned.

Tom covered the body so that it was decent, replaced the axle in his cart, and continued his journey to St Ives ('that old dirty town under the hill') where he delivered the beer and was then able to return to Market-jew before night-fall. The mayor was well pleased by Tom's efforts and urged him to continue working in the trade, but he refused saying that his great-grandfather had died unexpectedly and left him all his wealth so that he would have to return to the high country in order to look after it, and to bury the old man.

Tom and Jack the Tinkard

On his way back to the giant's castle Tom paused to say farewell to his old mammy, saying that he had met with a good place a long way off. Then he went to Crowlas to fetch his sweetheart, Joan, whom he had been courting a long time. He told her of his luck and that he had come to take her home, but he made no mention of his adventure to anyone else. They came to the castle and when they were called by name the dogs allowed them to enter without even a growl. Exploring the giant's home they found a fantastic fortune of treasure hidden in its cellars. Then they proceeded to bury Denbras in as noble a barrow as may be found in the Towednack hills, seating the body on a throne and placing an enormous capstone on upright stones to cover the grave (so making the traditional quoit).

Thus Tom and Joan began their life at the castle of the old giant. They were happy in their lonely existence and had many children. No visitors ever came to the castle as it was still believed that Denbras was alive. The children were weaned by nanny goats and thus grew up exceptionally strong, though some of the boys were so shaggy that they looked like their foster mothers. They were called Zennor goats, a term still in use to describe the unkempt today. By the time the boys were a year old they were able to help on the land, building the great hedges of rock that may still be seen in this countryside. It would take ten ordinary men to lift the great rocks that they positioned so easily on their own. But one day the isolation of the family came to an end when a tinker called at the castle. At first his reception by Tom was hostile but when he offered to fight for his right to enter the castle and sell his wares Tom was glad to accept the challenge. After a long series of contests (at which Tom was invariably the loser) the two became firm friends. Jack, for that was the tinkard's name, was urged to stay at the castle and eventually became betrothed to Tom's daughter, Genevra, and built a house for her at Chûn, close to Morvah. Like most folk of the time, Jack chose a hill-top site since the moors and cleared ground of the lowlands were so infested with adders that they were not only uninhabitable but also unsafe for cattle in the summer months.

As the time of the wedding approached Joan and Genevra began urging that the family should pay a visit to town in order to spend some of their riches on finery fitting for the occasion. At last Tom gave in to their arguments and sent Jack to Market-jew with some of their tin for smelting. The mayor of the town (the brewer who had engaged Tom to take ale to St Ives many years before) was bemused by the quality and quantity of the ore that Jack brought, and on hearing that it came from his acquaintance of long ago declared that a Smelting Feast should be held to celebrate Tom's good fortune and their reunion.

Preparations for the feast occupied the townsfolk for several weeks beforehand, and it turned out to be the most splendid festival in living memory. One of the distinguished guests was the Lord of Pengersec who was wealthy and of a strikingly handsome appearance who also had the reputation of being a powerful magician. He made much of Tom, sitting next to him at the banquet and persistently plying him with drink so that by the end of the day he was much the worse for its effects. Thus all the others returned home leaving Tom to sleep it off at the house of the mayor. When her husband failed to return the next morning Joan began to worry, blaming herself for contacting the outside world, feeling in her heart of hearts that no good would come of it. Late that day two figures were seen approaching the castle on horseback. One was the master of the house, the other was the enchanter Pengersec.

Jack's Encounter with Pengersec

Joan had good cause to worry about the friendship that had been struck between Tom and the sinister Lord of Pengersec. The latter had a powerful reputation for magic, being supposed to be able to raise the Devil or the dead with equal ease. He had so intimidated the old giant of St Michael's Mount that the poor old fellow no longer dared emerge from his lair on the Mount for fear of falling foul of Pengersec again. The first time that this had occurred was when the giant was seen by the magician to steal one of his bullocks (he had been warned by his familiars of the giant's intentions). He waited until the old giant had the bullock on a cliff-edge above the sea, about to settle it on his shoulders, and immediately he took the load Pengersec bewitched him so that he was paralysed at the bottom of the cliff-face, crouched with the struggling beast about his neck and with the tide rising steadily. But by magic the water stopped just short of drowning the ancient monster, though all through that night he suffered constant duckings with the sea water always surging against his lips. In the morning Pengersec brought his servants down to witness the fate of the unhappy giant, and as he released him from the spell they pelted him with stones and so drove him back to the Mount. The magician had built himself a tower where he was said to turn the clay of the earth to gold, assisted by familiar devils, while searing flames and clouds of smoke stinking of brimstone belched from the top of the tower. He also owned a magical glass with which he could draw on all the power of the sun, and so burn up his enemies' lands if he so wished.

Joan sent her daughter Genevra off to bed and set about preparing supper for the newcomers (the rest of the household had already eaten) saying that even if the Old One himself came to the castle he would have to be treated with good cheer. Meanwhile, Tom and Jack were showing the visitor their lands and livestock, and he charmed them by admiring these enthusiastically. Later he also won over Joan by praising the beauty of her children, the excellence of the food that she had prepared, and her taste in furnishing the place. However, though Jack, too, was captivated a part of him held back, for hidden in the deepest recesses of his soul was something that made him doubt the goodwill of the man.

After finishing the food that Joan had prepared they settled to an evening of music-making. Pengersec showed himself complete master of this craft and held the assembly enthralled for hours on end. At length Jack got up to check the animals and find the time of night by reading the position of the stars (for, of course, they had no clocks then). As he turned to re-enter the building he saw with surprise the magician's black stallion standing by the door, its eyes burning like coals of fire and the breath from its flared nostrils like the flames of sulphur. Then Jack entered the hall and there was Pengersec standing in the midst of clouds of smoke or vapour which spread throughout the castle with an intoxicating perfume. A metal band, set with seven precious stones, for the planetary signs, encircled the magician's head; his mantle, spread wide, showed round his waist the

broad leather girdle, on which were many strange magical figures; on his breast hung the magic pentagram; in his hand he grasped a strange wand which he was waving over Tom, Joan and the rest, who, all but Genevra, were laid on the ground as dead as the stones on which they lay.

Then Jack saw that his beloved Genevra had also come to the chamber but, mesmerised as he was by the fragrant incense, he was powerless to intervene in the events that followed. Briefly, as she saw Jack, she held out her arms towards him, but the power of the magician prevailed, and she walked, as in a dream, to his side. As Pengersec picked her off her feet she went limp as though dead, and he bore her off to his horse, leaving the room and closing the door behind him. This released Jack from the spell, and he ran from the hall after the enchanter, just in time to see him throw Genevra across his saddle and then climb up behind her. A train of blue fire marked their passage as they galloped off down the hillside to the lower gate. Here Pengersec had to stop for a moment: whether the demon steed was unable to rise off the earth with the innocent maiden, or Pengersec feared to take the leap with his precious burden, he did not attempt to spring his horse over the iron spikes that the tinkard had placed on the top of the gate, but tried in vain when he lifted the latch to push open the gate, for this was secured by a lock of the tinkard's contrivance, which could not be opened by anyone unacquainted with the secret of its construction. At the instant the magician bore off Genevra, Jack felt the charm-stone which had been hung on his neck when a child to protect him from evil leaping on his breast like a thing alive, as much as to say, 'Try *my* virtue when everything else has failed!' Jack had thought but little, and believed less, of what his mammy had told him about the virtue that abode in the bit of ironstone she hung on his chest. Yet now, quick as thought, he followed her directions, by first touching his forehead and mouth with the stone; then, when he placed it on his breast near the heart, he felt the courage of a lion; his lips were unsealed to speak a word that broke the spell, and his brain told him to use his bow – Jack aimed his arrow at the enchanter's naked left hand, stretched out to pull the bobbin that lifted the latch. It went right through the open hand and nailed it to the oaken gate: just as quickly as the arrow flew, Jack arrived, hammer in hand. With the first blow of the hammer he broke the enchanter's right arm; then he tore Genevra from his grasp, and laid her on the grass, to all appearance dead – then he gave a vigorous blow to the diamond star which blazed in the forehead of the steed, and with the ring of the hammer Jack spoke a word which makes the devils quake and tremble. The demon steed shrank to the ground like a shrivelled-up skin, which, in a twinkling, changed into a black adder that crawled away under the gate and left the rider hanging by his hand.

Next, ignoring Pengersec's pleas for mercy, Tom set about stripping him of the rest of his finery, which he knew was the secret of his magical powers. Bare of all his magical machinery Pengersec seemed changed from a big, dark, handsome man into an old, withered, ugly, filthy wretch, loathsome to behold; his sunken orbs gleamed in their sockets like the eyes of an adder ready to spring at its prey, as he slunk away, mumbling curses and threats of vengeance.

Jack's first care was to release Genevra from her enchanted trance by a counter-spell, and when this was accomplished by means of the potent fragment of ironstone suspended from his neck he turned his attention to the other members of the family still prostrate on the floor of the great hall. Miraculously, liberal applications of spring water soon brought them to their feet and everyone was soon clamouring around Jack asking so many questions that they were hard put to hear his answers.

Soon afterwards the wedding took place at Morvah, and such a happy festival was the subsequent feast that it was for ever after celebrated there on its anniversary, the first Sunday in August. Jack and Genevra lived at their house at Chûn and raised a large family, and by carefully managing the treasure that they inherited from the giant all eventually flourished on lands of their own. It is from this stock, from Tom and Joan, and from Jack and Genevra, that the oldest families in these parts are descended. In later years, when the doughty deeds of Jack the Tinkard (or Jack the Hammer, as he was also known) were only imperfectly remembered by his descendants, they, for more glory, made him out to be a giant, just as they have magnified the deeds and made giants of many other heroes; and Jack (if anything like the character given of him in the old folks' drolls) was worth a bundle of many old giants, as they by most accounts, did little more than hurl great rocks from hill to hill, or play bob with the quoits they have left about among the cairns.

The Giants of Castle Treen

Old traditions say that the headlands of Castle Treen, or rather Trereen, on which the Logan Rock carn and adjacent crags stand, was raised out of the sea by enchantment. This portion of the stronghold, enclosed by the inner line of defence, running directly across the isthmus, is generally spoken of as the Castle, and that between it and the outer or landward embankments is usually called Treen Dynas.

It is not known what powerful magician raised this giant's hold, though it was believed that its security depended on a magic stone called 'the key of the castle', respecting which Merlin had something to say, as well as about many other remarkable stones in the neighbourhood. Castle Treen, however, must have stood where it is long before Arthur and his magician visited West Cornwall.

The key was an egg-shaped stone, between two and three feet long, which was contained in the cavity of a rock with a hole facing the sea, through which it might be turned round; and the opening appeared large enough for it to be passed through. Many attempted to get it out, but they always found it to hitch somewhere; and lucky (according to old folks' faith) that it did, because the sage Merlin prophesied that when the key of the castle was taken out of the hole, Men Amber (the holy rock) would be overthrown, the castle sink beneath the ocean, and other calamities occur.

The key was situated near the bottom of a deep chasm called the Gap, which is passed on approaching the Logan Rock by the usual path. It required a sure-footed climber, of strong nerve, to reach it, and this could only be done from land, at low water, or nearly so.

Surging waves occasionally changed the position of this magic stone, and from the direction of its smaller end, as it lay in a trough of water, prognostics were drawn with regard to the seasons, etc.

Few persons had sufficient hardihood to descend the precipitous cliff and risk being caught in the Gap by a flowing tide; and the key of the castle remained a mysterious and venerated object till

Goldsmith's mischievous tars, or the dockyard men who were employed in erecting machinery to replace Men Amber (as the stone they overthrew was formerly called) heard of it and the traditions connected therewith.*

Then one day, some of these wretches, on further mischief bent, entered the Gap in a boat, and, being provided with crowbars, they broke away the edges of the rock that enclose the key, ripped it out, and tumbled it down among the sea-washed pebbles. Some calamity has surely befallen these wretches ere this, or Bad Luck is a mere name, and powerless as an avenging deity.

Part of Merlin's prophecy was fulfilled, however, yet not in the order predicted. The venerated nodule was what is called, among miners, a 'bull's eye', or 'pig's egg', of large size. It appeared to be a closer-grained and harder stone than what surrounded it.

* 'This celebrated Logan Rock, which is calculated to weigh 80 tons, was forced from its equilibrium on 8th April 1824 through the excessive vibration given to it by the united manual exertions of nine persons. It was restored to its former situation on the 2nd of November following by the skilful application of Machinery, and the labour of upwards of fifty persons, under the sole direction of Lieutenant Goldsmith, R.N.' (*The Graphic*, 25 November 1893)
Goldsmith, the nephew of the poet, was the leader of the 'mischievous tars' who displaced the Rock in the first place. The Admiralty made him pay for its restoration though it was never again so perfectly balanced.

The earliest inhabitants of this stronghold were giants who protected the neighbouring people in return for cattle and other necessaries. An aged giant, his childless wife, and their adopted son are the only ones of whom connected traditions are handed down by old folks of Treen. Not only this giant (how we wish the chroniclers had preserved his name) and his wife but all people who depended on his protection, particularly those of Treen and bordering places, were much grieved when they found their giant and giantess were middle-aged and had no children who would aid them in old age and perpetuate the race.

The giantess, having no household to think about, grew, as most unemployed women do, peevish and troublesome. The giant, having little or no work to occupy himself with, grew fat and lazy. Quiet and good tempered as he was, he was dreadfully tormented by his wife. She called him a lazy, useless old loon; and said he was too fat, and didn't take exercise enow. When he had nothing else to employ himself about, in peaceful times, she told him that he should log the rock, for a few hours each day, to stretch his sinews and make his blood circulate brisker, instead of dozing away all day and night in his chair, which may still be seen. It was easy for him to do this – with the tip of his finger on the top of Men Amber he could walk around the

rock on the grassy sward below, for the rock is only thirty feet high from the grass and Treen giant stood at least forty feet high, without his boots. He was stout in proportion, and his strength of arm was prodigious. Sometimes, with his staff, he kept the sacred stone in motion when seated in his chair, just opposite it. But often it happened, when getting through his exercise by the latter mode, that he fell asleep, long ere the sand was down in his wife's hour-glass. And then she, the faggot, would pelt her quiet husband with rocks, heaps of which may still be seen, lying loose, just as they flew from her hand and dropped at no great distance from the poor giant's chair. He would wake up, with a sore head, to hear her say, in a voice like a bellowing bull, 'Stop thy snoring, thou confounded old fool, and work away, west ah? or I'll pommel thy noddle to browse.'

'What the deuce shall I do to stop her tongue and cure her temper? Can 'e tell me, my good people?' he would often say to Treen folks and others, who visited him of a summer's evening; 'she's the most troublesome woman I ever heard of.'

All kinds of employment were suggested. In those days everybody thought he could manage a discontented wife, were he her husband; but actually to do it was difficult. Potent reasons were given both by giantess and people why they desired that their chief's race should be continued. Charms and other means were used in order to obtain the desired result.

Yet much time passed, and their rock-hewn cradle was still empty, when a happy thought struck a wise man of Treen. He advised that a baby should be stolen from the giant of Maen (Mayon), who had a large family, and was, moreover, a very troublesome and aggressive neighbour – if one may credit stories of his hurling rocks against the Treen giant, which are still to be seen at Skewjack Moor, on the bounds of their two domains. One may judge the Maen giant's stature by the size of his bed, bowls, spoon and other utensils, that remained in a lane on Treve, at a short distance from Sennen Church, a few years ago, and some of them may still be there.

Our giant and his wife were delighted with the sage man's advice. To steal a baby from the big man who was proud of his stronghold between Pen-von-las (Land's End) and Pedn-men-du (Black Stone Headland) would be capital revenge on him and his. A wise woman, or witch of Treen, who could take any shape, was selected as the most likely person to execute their project without causing any stir with the Maen giant, who was very fierce, and proud of his descent from old blustering Bellerus, who was said to have lived thereabouts in days of yore.

The witch took herself off to Sennen one afternoon when she knew that the baby was busy playing with the children of the village. It was a simple task to lure him away from them, and they travelled back to Treen together, she keeping him amused by assuming a variety of different shapes, though most often she was a horse so that he might ride on her back. At last she led him into Castle Treen where he was received with open arms by the mistress.

It would take a long time to tell how he was caressed by the childless pair and fed by their people. He often reposed, during his infancy, in a small chair that may still be seen near the large one in which the giant usually rested – the one just opposite the Logan Rock; and, until he grew too big, he frequently slept in the giant's arms.

When a few years older the giant taught his big boy to fish from the rocks with rod and line, showed him how to make fish-hooks out of bones and *croggan* – rims – as boys out there do now, or did, not long ago. In giants' times they hadn't a bit of iron, not even so much as a nail. The giantess, with her distaff and spindle, spun them yarn that served for lines. Meanwhile, the giantess took care that the boy had an unlimited quantity of food, that he might eat and drink whenever he choose. Over a few years he was almost equal in bulk to his new Dadda, as he called the old giant. We like to linger over these pleasant times, for the old Titan took much delight in his charge. But alas! the sequel must be told in sorrow and tears for female frailty. We do not like to – and indeed we will not – repeat all the stories handed down, which for the most part are highly unfavourable to the moral character of the Treen giantess, for fear of slandering her unwittingly. Yet it is no worse than she deserves to say that all traditions agree in representing her as a most abandoned female in her latter years.

All her care and attention were bestowed on the boy and she neglected her old husband, so that he had to dive for fish, and skin oxen (or eat them skin, horns and all). Sheep he could seldom get; they were dainties reserved for the young fellow. The poor old giant was often driven to such extremities that, to appease hunger, he stayed his stomach on ore-weed. To add insult to injury she often taunted her aged spouse with his weakness, which was the consequence of her neglect, and cut him to the heart by making unfavourable comparisons between him and the pampered youth who could now log the rock from sitting on the grass; and that was more, as the giantess told her husband, than he could do in the best of his time. Worst of all, her maternal love then changed into a passion that, all things considered, one might even now, in these times of lax morality and free-love, regard as reprehensible.

The old giant was slow to become jealous, till he found himself utterly forsaken by his spouse and adopted son, who always stole away to sunny glades between the carns to play by themselves. That would have passed, however, without notice – he rather liked to be left alone, to doze in his chair of afternoons – had not some Treen women, who were sharp in such things, spied what was going on, and, out of envy, told the old giant. He then became very surly and gave the doting pair much annoyance by coming on them unawares when they withdrew to enjoy their amorous diversion. They had seldom much comfort then, except when the old fellow left his castle to get provision.

One winter's day, when he was about to start for this purpose, he told his wife and the youngster that one of them should meet him on his way back to assist in taking home whatever he might procure. They promised to do so, but time passed so pleasantly with the couple that they thought but little of their good old provider till they heard his footsteps and angry voice, about a quarter of a mile off, as he came stamping along Pedn-y-vounder cliff vowing vengeance on his ungrateful wife and foster-son.

They became somewhat frightened, and the giantess prepared for the encounter by placing herself on the rocks west of the Gap, a dozen feet or so above the narrow path which the giant would have to pass. He came stamping along, an ox on his shoulders (its legs were tied together and passed over his head) and on each arm he carried a sheep basket-fashion, their trotters bound with their spans.

He roared louder than the stormy breakers when he entered his castle's inner enclosure and found that no one, even then, came to meet him. In his fury he bounced along without noticing his wicked rib, with her bared arm and clenched fist, awaiting his approach, and as he came along the narrow ledge she dealt him a blow in the eyes, as he glanced towards her, that sent him, cattle and all, heels over head down the precipice.

When she beheld him falling, a remembrance of their early loves, or something else, caused a sudden revulsion of feeling, which made her regret her rashness, and, unwilling to witness her husband's dying agony, she stepped back westwards, about twenty paces, on to a level stone between high rocks, where she stood still and cast her apron over her head that she might hear less of the giant's awful moans. Though the giant's skull was very thick it was badly smashed on the boulders; yet he didn't die until he called on the Powers whom he served to avenge him, which they did instantly by changing his vile partner into stone, where she stood and where she may still be seen. The old giant, in his dying moments, could not, in his heart, feel very bitter against the simple-minded hobble-de-hoy, and regarded his wife as the seducer.

Of late the Giant's Lady, as she was formerly called, has been named the Logan Rock's Lady by those who are ignorant of our old traditions. When tempests rage, or anything else excites her, she rocks to and fro; but her movements are languid with age or sorrow. Pitiless storms have so beaten on her head for ages that one cannot make out a feature, and her fair proportions are so mutilated that one can scarce discern a semblance of her gigantic form in the time-worn granite mass. She appears, indeed, of pigmy stature compared with her husband. If, however, she had never been larger than her stone image now appears the story is none the less credible on that score. For do we not, every day, see mere midges of women united with giants of men, according to our reduced scale?

Dan Dynas

Old Folks held – and long tradition made it pass for true – that the outer wall of Castle Treen was built by a deaf-and-dumb giant called Dan Dynas, or, as some say, Den-an-Dynas, assisted by his wife An' (aunt) Venna, who broke up the ditch, filled her leather towser (large apron) with the soil, and put it for filling behind the rocks, as her husband rolled them into their places. When they had thus constructed a stronghold, in which people with their tin and cattle were safe from marauding pirates, the giantess and other women collected hundreds of cartloads of stones into heaps near the mound, ready for slinging at, or dropping on, the heads of besiegers. When an incursion happened to be made An' Venna, with the women and old men, defended the fortress, while Dan and his fighting men slew the enemy or drove them to sea. The ruins of this good couple's handiwork may still be traced from Par Pry, on the southern side, to the inlet of Gampar, or Hal-dynas Cove, towards the east. (Marked as *Treryn Dinas* on Ordnance Survey, *ed.*)

A descendant of old proprietors of Treen informed me that a great quantity of stones remained, in piles, within and near the embankment, until after wheel carriages came into use. Although this part of the cliff was then common few persons cared to remove them, and none durst take a stone from the castle walls for fear Bad Luck would pursue anyone who disturbed the giant's work, But of late years, great portions of this ancient rampart have been demolished and its facing-stones carried away for building.

It is also related – though the story seems rather fabulous – that this deaf-and-dumb giant would stand on Carnole and thence sink invading ships entering Parcurno (Porthcurno), by hurling rocks on them, or he wrecked them, when at a distance, with huge stones discharged from slings made of bulls' hides. When the people could not charge his instruments of war as quickly as he wanted them, he would roar like thunder, make signs to stand clear, kick the rocks up out of the ground, smash them to handy pieces, and fire away again.

Like all other West Country giants he was very fond of old-fashioned games, and was delighted when youngsters came down to Kaer Keis of an afternoon to play quoits or ninepins with him; but he could never understand the weakness of ordinary mortals' frames; for, in caressing his playmates, he now and then broke their ribs or cracked their skulls – to his great grief and greater surprise. We may remark that, although some of the Cornish giants have been misrepresented as little better than savage cannibals – Cormovan of the Mount to wit – all traditional giant stories, in this district, describe them as amiable protectors of the common folks who lived near their castles. They were, however, almost invariably stupid, and often did mischief unwittingly by having more strength than sense; therefore it is shameful to defame those ancient heroes and ascribe to them such vile traits as are not warranted by our popular stories.

Carn Galva – the Giant of the Carn

By the traditions, still preserved in Morvah, the Giant of Carn Galva was more playful than warlike. Though the old works of the giant now stand desolate, we may still see, or get up and rock ourselves upon, the logan stone which this dear old giant placed on the most westerly carn of the range, that he might log himself to sleep when he saw the sun dip into the waves and the sea-birds fly to their homes in the cleaves. Near the giant's rocking-seat, one may still see a pile of cubical rocks, which are almost as regular and shapely now as when the giant used to amuse himself in building them up and knocking them down again, for exercise or play, when alone and he had nothing else to do. The people of the northern hills have always had a loving regard for the memory of this giant, because he appears to have passed all his life at the carn in single blessedness, merely to protect his beloved people of Morvah and Zennor from the depradations of the less honest Titans who then dwelt on Lelant hills. Carn Galva giant never killed but one of the Morvah people in his life, and that happened all through loving play.

The giant was very fond of a fine young fellow, of Choon, who used to take a turn over to the carn, every now and then, just to see how the old giant was getting on, to cheer him up a bit, to play a game of bob, or anything else to help him pass his lonely time away. One afternoon the giant was so well pleased with the good play they had together that, when the young fellow of Choon threw down his quoit to go away home, the giant, in a good-natured way, tapped his playfellow on the head with the tips of his fingers. At the same time he said, 'Be sure to come again tomorrow, my son, and we will have a capital game of bob.' Before the word 'bob' was well out of the giant's mouth, the young man dropped at his feet – the giant's fingers had gone right through his playmate's skull. When, at last, the giant became sensible of the damage he had done to the brain-pan of the young man, he did his best to put the inside workings of his mate's head to rights and plugged up his finger-holes, but all to no purpose; for the young man was stone dead, long before the giant ceased doctoring his head.

When the poor giant found it was all over with his playmate, he took the body in his arms, and sitting down on the large square rock at the foot of the carn, he rocked himself to and fro; pressing the lifeless body to his bosom, he wailed and moaned over him, bellowing and crying louder than the booming billows breaking on the rocks in Permoina (Porthmoina Cove).

'Oh, my son, my son, why didn't they make the shell of thy noddle stronger? It's as plum (soft) as a pie-crust, dough-baked, and made too thin by half! How shall I ever pass the time without thee to play bob and mop-and-heede (hide-and-seek)?'

The giant of Carn Galva never rejoiced any more, but, in seven years or so, he pined away and died of a broken heart. So the Morvah people say – and that one may judge of the size of their giant very well, as he placed his logan rock at such a height that, when seated on it, to rock himself, he could rest his feet comfortably on the green turf below.

Some, also, say that he gathered together the heap of square blocks, near his favourite resting-place, that he might have them at hand to defend his Morvah people against the giants of Trecrobben and Trink, with whom he fought many a hard battle. Yet when they were all on good terms they would pass weeks on a stretch playing together, and the quoits which served them to play bob, as well as the rocks they hurled at each other when vexed, may still be seen scattered all over this hilly region.

The Giants of Trecrobben and the Mount

Some of the giant race were still to be found in the high countries a few centuries ago, who had six fingers on each hand and six toes on each foot, but they were much smaller than their forefathers. In old times one of this extra-fingered, double-jointed race lived in his castle on Croben-hill, at the same time that a cousin of his kept house in a cavern of the Mount, about three miles from Trencrom. These two giants being on very friendly terms made one cobbling-hammer serve for the use of both. This hammer they used to throw forth and back between the Mount and Trencrom, as either happened to want it. One afternoon the giant of the Mount called from the mouth of his cave, 'Hallo up there, Trecrobben, throw us down the hammer, west ah?' 'Iss, in a minute; look sharp and catch en,' says he.

It so happened that the wife of Carreg-Cowse (as the giant of the Mount was called), having her full share of curiosity, wanted to see

Trecrobben, to ask after his old woman, and to know what was going on up among the hills. The sun shining bright at the time dazzled her eyes when she came out of her dark cave, and before she had the time to shade her face with her apron, while she was poking in her husband's way, down came the hammer, whack, hit her right between the eyes, and settled her. The noise the giants made in mourning over the death of the giantess was dreadful to hear – the roaring of Tregagle was nothing to their bellowing, which echoed from hill to hill. Trecrobben buried his treasures deep among the cairns of his castle, and grieved himself to death for the misfortune to his old crony's wife. Every now and then, down to the present time, many persons have dug all about the cairns on Trencrom, of moonshiny nights, in hopes of finding the crocks of gold that the giant buried there, but whenever they dig so deep as to touch the flat stone that covers the mouth of the crock, and hear it ring hollow, out from among the crevices of the rocks and cairns come troops of frightful-looking spriggens (goblins) who raise such dreadful weather that it scares the diggers away.

The Giant Wrath of Portreath

In old times there lived in a cavern on the seashore, about ten miles to the east of Hayle, a giant called Wrath, who had a bad character given him by the people of St Ives. Folks did not believe half the evil they said of him, but their fears of the giant, when alive, made them take the dastardly revenge of abusing him when dead. Yet whether he liked or disliked them it's hard to say, because if he killed them he ate them, according to their own accounts. The place in which Wrath lived is the fissure or gorge near Portreath known by the name of the Giant's Zawn, or more generally by that of Ralph's Cupboard. This latter name, of recent date, was given to the place after it had been inhabited by one Ralph, a famous smuggler who found the place most convenient for his trade. By being better acquainted than most other persons with the reefs and currents on this rock-strewn coast, Ralph did not fear to run his little vessel into the gorge on the darkest nights, safely land his goods, and whistle at the King's men. In the time of the giant Wrath this remarkable gorge was a deep cavern or zawn, into which the sea flowed, as it does still at high tide. The roof has fallen in since the death of the giant. Here Wrath would lie in wait and watch for any ships or fishing boats from St Ives that might come sailing by. If they approached within a mile of his holt, he would wade out, tap the fishermen or sailors on the head with the tip of his finger to settle them, then tie the ships and boats to his girdle, and quietly draw them to his den. He would save for provision the well-fed and fleshy men – the lean ones he threw overboard.

Ships bound for St Ives, sailing in too deep water for him to reach by wading, he sunk by slinging rocks on them from the cliff above. Many of these rocks may still be seen above water at ebb-tide, and form a dangerous reef stretching away from Godrevy Head. Long after the death of the giant, his holt was the terror of the fishermen of St Ives, who always avoided the Cupboard, as they said that nothing ever came out of it that had the bad luck to get into it.

The Giant Bolster of St Agnes

Only a few giants' steps from Portreath there dwelt in St Agnes another huge giant called Bolster, who made nothing of striding from the Beacon to Carn Brea – a distance of six miles, or more. The St Agnes people say that Bolster fell in love with their beautiful saint, who was a pattern woman of virtue. We think that monkish invention is apparent in this legend, because our real old giants were never the fools to waste their wind in filling the air with such a tempest of groans and sighs as Bolster is said to have blown after the cruel St Agnes, who served her tall lover, at last, too treacherous a trick, as an honest body might think, for any female saint to invent. After coquetting with the giant, she asked him, as a last proof of his love, to fill the hole in the cliff at Chapel Porth with his blood. The giant, thinking he could spare blood enough to fill many such holes. without

hesitation stretched his great arm over the hole, plunged a knife into a vein, and torrents of blood gushed out and flowed into the hole. The love-sick giant, ready to do anything to please the fancy of the fair saint, bled himself to death without discovering that, as fast as the seething gore issued from his arm, it ran into the sea through a hole in the bottom of the pit. The cunning saint, well aware that the hole had an opening at the bottom into the sea, thus got rid of her hill-striding lover.

Some may think that St Agnes served Bolster no worse than he deserved, because he was a married man all the time that he per-secuted the blessed saint with his troublesome love; besides, he was a most cruel husband. While he was going over the hills galivanting the saint, he compelled the unfortunate giantess to pick all the stones from the ground at the foot of Bury-Anack (as the Beacon was called in Bolster's time), on the side of the hill nearest to St Agnes town. She was made to carry the stones in her apron to the top of the hill, where they may still be seen, forming many burrows. She laboured so diligently that, at this day, the farm which is now made out of this part of the giant's land is remarkably clear of stones, although all the surrounding farms are as stony as the Fourborough Downs. Bolster himself, before he became enamoured of St Agnes, must have been an industrious, hard-working giant, enough to throw up the great gurgoe or stone hedge, miles long, that is still called by his name. Anyone who will take the trouble to go to St Agnes may still see a great part of this earthwork which, when he completed it, extended from Trevaunce Porth to Chapel Porth, enclosing all the richest tin-ground on the giant's land. As a proof of the truth of the tradition respecting the way in which the giant Bolster came by his death, the inhabitants of these parts still show the red stains in the hole at Chapel Porth, marking the track of the giant's gore which fell in torrents and flowed for hours down the hole.

The Small People
(and others)

The Fairy Tribes

According to the Fairy belief of the old Cornish folk, the Piskey has seldom been seen in any other shape than that of a weird, wizened-looking, little old man. As such he has often been spied of moonlight winter's nights threshing the corn in the barns of lonely places. Boslow and Lejarn are often spoken of as favourite haunts of this goblin. Another of his well-known pranks is to mount on the necks of the colts, where he plaits his Piskey stirrups in the winter, and rides the colts after the cows like mad in the summer. The leading of folks into the bogs, by appearing like a person with a lantern, or a light from a window, was a constant occurrence unless the night wanderer took the precaution to turn some garment inside out, to break the spell. The Piskey always wanders alone and is always spoken of in the singular. It is somewhat remarkable that a green bug, frequently found on bramble bushes in the autumn, is called by this name. After Michaelmas, it is said, the blackberries are unwholesome because Piskey spoils them then.

The Spriggans, quite a different class of beings, are the *dourest* and most ugly set of sprights belonging to the elfin tribe; they are only seen about old ruins, barrows, giants' quoits and castles, or other places where treasure is buried, of which they have the charge. Not long since a tinner of Lelant dreamt, three nights following, that a crock of gold was buried in a particular spot, between large rocks within the castle on Trecrobben hill. The next clear moonlight night he dug the ground of which he had dreamt. After working two or three hours he came to a flat stone which sounded hollow; while digging round its edges, the weather suddenly became dark, the wind roared around the carns, and looking up, when he had made a place to lift it, he saw hundreds of ugly Spriggans coming out from amid the rocks gathering around and approaching him. The man dropped his pick, ran down the hill as fast as he could lay foot to ground; he took to his bed and was unable to leave it for weeks. When he next visited the castle he found the pit all filled in, with the turf replaced, and he

never more dug for treasure. Spriggans also steal children, leaving their own ugly brats in their place, bring bad weather to blight the crops, whirlwinds over the fields of cut corn, and do much other mischief to those who meddle with their favourite haunts.

The innocent Small People, on the contrary, are always described as being extremely beautiful by all who have had the luck to see them, holding their merry fairs and sprightly dances on the velvety turf of the greens, sheltered glades between the cairns, or in other secluded pleasant places, dressed in their bright green nether garments, sky-blue jackets, three-cornered hats on the men, and pointed ones for the ladies, all decked with lace and silver bells. They are as lovely as the flowers of the fields. These good small folks often showed great kindness to those people to whom they took a fancy, and have frequently been known to come into poor cottages, divert good old bedridden folks with their merry pranks and gambols, and fill the air with the delicious odours of flowers, and such sweet melody as few but angels ever hear and live. A few days since, a woman of Mousehole told me that not long ago troops of Small People, no more than a foot and a half high, used on moonlight nights to come out of a hole in the cliff that opened on to the beach on the Newlyn side of the village. The little people were always dressed very smart, and if anyone came near them they would scamper away into the hole. Mothers often told their children that if they went under the cliff by night the Small People would carry them away into 'Dicky Danjy's holt'. Places frequented by goats are believed to be the favourite haunts of fairies.

The Bockles, or Knockers, can scarcely be classed as fairies; they seem rather to be a hybrid race between ordinary ghosts and elves, as

the miners believe them to be the restless souls of the Jews who formerly worked the tin-mines of Cornwall. The tinners often hear them working underground; sometimes these ghostly workers may be heard even from the surface, yet they so rarely make their appearance now that we hardly know what they are like.

It is also uncertain whether the Bucca can be regarded as one of the fairy tribe. Old people within my remembrance spoke of a Bucca Gwidden and a Bucca Dhu – by the former they meant a good spirit, and by the latter an evil one, now known as Bucca-boo. I have been told by persons of credit that within the last forty years it was the usual practice with Newlyn and Mousehole fishermen to leave on the sand at night a portion of their catch for Bucca.

There are a few other mythical beings belonging to our elvin creed but they too have been so seldom seen of latter days that very little is known of the Browneys, Mermaids, etc. Probably the Mermaids so much dislike steamships that the fair syrens have taken themselves off, with all their combs and glasses, to the China Seas, so as to be out of the way of the fiery monsters of the deep.

The Mermaid of Zennor

Hundreds of years ago a very beautiful and richly attired lady attended service in Zennor Church occasionally – now and then she went to Morvah also. Her visits were by no means regular – often long intervals would elapse between them.

Yet whenever she came the people were enchanted with her good looks and sweet singing. Although Zennor folks were remarkable for their fine psalmody, she excelled them all; and they wondered how,

after the scores of years that they had seen her, she continued to look so young and fair. No one knew whence she came or whither she went; yet many watched her as far as they could from Tregarthen Hill.

She took some notice of a fine young man, called Mathey Trewella, who was the best singer in the parish. He once followed her, but never returned; after that she was never more seen in Zennor Church, and it might not have been known to this day who or what she was but for the merest accident.

One Sunday morning a vessel cast anchor about a mile from Pendower Cove; soon after a mermaid came alongside and hailed the ship. Rising out of the water as far as her waist, with her yellow hair floating around her, she told the captain that the anchor was dropped on the trap-door that gave access to her submarine abode. On returning from her fishing, she found she was hindered from entering her door and begged the captain to raise the anchor so that she might get in to her children.

Her polite request had a magical effect upon the sailors, for they immediately worked with a will to hove anchor and set sail, not wishing to remain a moment longer than they could help near her habitation. Seafaring men, who understood most about mermaids, regarded their appearance as a token that bad luck was near at hand. It was believed they could take such shapes as suited their purpose, and that they had often allured men to live with them.

When Zennor folks learnt that a mermaid dwelt near Pendower, and what she had told the captain, they concluded that it was this sea-lady who had visited their church and enticed Trewella to her abode. To commemorate these somewhat unusual events they had the figure she bore – when in her ocean home – carved in holy oak, which may still be seen on a bench-end in their church.

The Hooper of Sennen Cove

Within easy memory many parts of the western coast were said to be frequented by mermaids, particularly Sennen Cove. This place was also resorted to by a remarkable spirit called the Hooper – from the hooting or hooping sounds which it was accustomed to make.

In old time, according to tradition, a compact cloud of mist often came in from over the sea – when the weather was by no means foggy – and rested on the rocks called Cowloe, thence it spread itself, like a curtain of cloud, quite across Sennen Cove. By night a dull light was mostly seen amid the vapour, with sparks ascending as if a fire burned within it; at the same time hooping sounds were heard proceeding therefrom. People believed the misty cloud shrouded a spirit, which came to forewarn them of approaching storms, and that those who attempted to put to sea found an invisible force – seemingly in the mist – to resist them.

A reckless fisherman and his son, however – disregarding the token – launched their boat and beat through the fog with a flail; they passed the cloud of mist which followed them, and neither the men, nor the Hooper, were evermore seen in Sennen Cove.

This is the only place in the west where any tradition of such a guardian spirit is preserved.

The Men-an-Tol and other Monuments

In a croft belonging to Lanyon farm, and about half a mile north of the town-place, there is a remarkable group of three stones, the centre one of which is called by antiquaries the Men-an-tol (holed stone), and by country folks the Crick-stone, from an old custom, not yet extinct, of crawling on all fours nine times through the hole in the centre stone, going against the sun's course, for the cure of lumbago, sciatica, and other 'cricks' and pains to the back. Young children were also put through it to ensure healthy growth. A similar superstition said that a cure for boils and rheumatism was to crawl beneath a bramble growing at both ends nine times against the sun. The notion is that going against the sun will backen a disease but in all other cases the sun's course must be followed.

The holed stones at Madron and Constantine were held to have like properties. I was told that some remarkable cures had been effected at the latter only a few weeks since. The ceremony here consists of passing a child (suffering from an ailment of the back) nine times through the hole, alternatively from one side to the other; and it is essential to the success of the operation that it should finish on that side where there is a little grassy mound, recently made, on which the patient must sleep, with a sixpence under his head. A trough-like stone, called the 'cradle', on the eastern side of the barrow, was formerly used for this purpose. This stone, unfortunately, has long been destroyed. That holed stones were not originally constructed for the observance of this peculiar custom is evident, for in some instances the holes are not more than five or six inches in diameter.

On the southern side of the highway from Lamorna to the Land's End, at about three miles from St Buryan, is the circle of upright stones known by local inhabitants as the Daunce-Mayn. The name is most probably a curruption of Zans Mêyn (sacred stones) and has nothing whatever to do with dancing maids any more than dairy maids. The legend that the (originally) nineteen posts were damsels, thus fixed for dancing on Sunday, was evidently suggested by the name to some manufacturer of such wares, who as readily converted the two longstones, in the field across the road, into the Pipers, who took to their heels and left the damsels to their fate as soon as their metamorphosis began; but their ungallant action did not avail, as the petrifying power of the cursing saint (St Levan), who stopped their sweet pipings, overtook them when they ran thus far, and laid them up in stone as we now see them.

No such legend, however, is native to the place, as the old folk only know it from having it repeated to them by visitors, who have seen it in books. The Menhere (menhirs), changed into Pipers, were known to them by the name of the Hurlers, from their having been a goal for the hurling-run, when the starting-post (where the ball was thrown up) was the cross in the churchtown.

Another common name for the Celtic circles is the Nine Maidens. Now, as the usual number of stones in the circle is nineteen, that number may have something to do with the first part of this name, and the latter would come from the Cornish 'mêdn' an alternative spelling of 'mêyn'.

The Daunce-Mêyn is the best known of all the Druidic circles in the west, as it is within sight of the road frequently taken by those visitors to the Logan Rock who care to see the many interesting objects, and fine sea views, visible from the lower road, as we call this route near the seashore. Yet the circle at Boscawen (on the high road to Land's End) is also invested with great interest. Fortunately the work of destruction has been arrested at this circle, as the lady to whom the property belongs has caused it to be surrounded with a good hedge to prevent further spoliation. Some years ago a wholesome fear prevailed of an avenging deity that would bring disaster to anyone who moved these landmarks of a long past age. But now our country folk think themselves more enlightened and exercise their vandalism on the monuments of ancient times: pages might be filled with an account of the destruction which has taken place within the past half century.

About a furlong south-west of Trove, but on a tenement of Boleigh, is the Fuggo. It consists of a cave about six feet high, five feet wide, and near forty long, faced on each side with rough stones, across which long stone posts are laid. On its north-western side a narrow passage leads into another cave of similar construction and unknown extent, as it has long been blocked up by a portion of the roof having fallen in. One may be pretty sure, however, that many of the stories of its great length are fabulous. They say that it extends from its entrance at the foot of Boleigh hill to the old mansion at Trove; in proof of this the Old One has often been heard piping under a parlour of the house. It is supposed he meets the witches down there who have entered the Fuggo to dance to his music. Hares are often seen to enter the Fuggo which are never seen to come out the same way; they are said to be witches going to meet their master who provides them with some other shape to return in. There are also traditions of this cavern having served as a place of refuge to some of the Levelis in troublesome times, and of its having frequently been used by our fair-traders, as it afforded them a secure hold for storing their goods, and to have a carouse therein.

A short time ago an old inhabitant of Boleigh informed us that many persons in that neighbourhood are afraid to enter the Fuggo, even by day, as they believe that bad spirits still frequent the place. Women of villages near often threaten their crying babies that they will carry them down to the Fuggo and leave them there for the Bucca-boo if they do not stop their squalling. There are traditions that almost all these caves were haunted by beings of a fearful nature whose path it was dangerous to cross.

The Fuggo at Bodinnar, called the Giant's Holt, was a few years ago much dreaded as it was thought to be the abode of ugly spriggans that kept watch and guard over treasures which still remain buried in that ancient hiding-place.

There is a somewhat graceful creation of fancy associated with the Vow, or Fuggo, at Pendeen, which is said to extend from the mansion to Pendeen Cove, and some say it has branches in other directions, which spread far away from the principal cavern. At dawn the 'Spirit of the Vow' has frequently been seen just within the entrance, near the Cove, in the form of a beautiful lady, dressed in white, with a red rose in her mouth. There were persons living, a few years since, who had seen this fair but not the less fearful vision, for disaster was sure to visit those who intruded on the spirit's morning airings.

The Small People's Cow

There is a story connected with the Pendars which says that, when this family was on its wane, the owner of Baranhual had a fine red cow, called Rosy, which gave twice as much milk as an ordinary one. She retained her milk-yielding power all the year through and kept in good condition, even in winter, when other cattle on better food were reduced to skin and bone. Rosy would yield all her morning's milk, but every evening when much – and that the richest – still remained in her udder, she would stop chewing her cud, cock her ears, low gently as if calling a calf, and the 'shower' of milk would cease. If the maid attempted to renew her milking Rosy would kick the bucket and gallop away to a remote part of the field.

Dame Pendar, thinking the milkmaid did not shake Rosy's bag and coax her enough, tried, one evening, what she could do; but when she began 'visting' Rosy's teats to get more milk, after the cow's usual signal to cease, she up foot and smashed the wooden pail to pieces, tossed Dame Pendar over her back, and, bellowing, raced away – tail on end.

Though Rosy kept in milk when all other cows were gone dry, yet, because there was something strange about her, after she had given the dame a tossing, an attempt was made to get her to market; but all the people on Baranhual could not drive her off the farm.

Over a while Rosy had a heifer calf, and when it had sucked its fill, its dam gave her usual quantity of milk into the bucket, and then enough remained to fill another. Stranger still, in a few weeks the calf could eat herbage, and its dam weaned it gradually, but it could never be separated from her.

Everything prospered with Mr Pendar. His cattle and crops throve wonderfully, till one midsummer's night. His milkmaid had gone to games held at Penberth and only returned when the stars began to blink. Rosy, impatient to be milked, came to meet her in the field, stood still, placed back her leg, chewed her cud, and showered her milk into the bucket till she had yielded more than usual: then she

stretched herself, looked around, and gently lowed while the maid, without rising from her milking-stool, pulled up a handful of grass, rolled it into a pad and placed it inside her hat, that she might carry her bucket the steadier. Having put on her hat she was surprised to see hundreds of 'Small People' (fairies) around the cow, and on her back, head and neck. A great number of little beings – as many as could get under Rosy's udder at once – held buttercups and other handy flowers or leaves, twisted into drinking vessels, to catch the shower of milk that fell among them, and some sucked it from clover-blossoms. As one set walked off satisfied, others took their places. They moved about so quickly that the milkmaid's head got almost 'light' while she looked at them. 'You should have seen,' said the maid afterwards, 'how pleased Rosy looked, as she tried to lick those on her neck who scratched her behind the horns or picked ticks from her ears; while others, on her back, smoothed down every hair of her coat.

They made much of the calf too; and, when they had their fill of milk, one and all brought their little arms full of herbs to Rosy and her calf – how they licked all up and asked for more!''

Some little folk, who came late, were mounted on hares, which they left to graze a few yards from the cow.

For a good while the milkmaid stood, with the bucket on her head, like one spellbound, looking at the Small People; and she would have continued much longer to admire, but, just as some came within a yard of her, Dame Pendar suddenly stood up on the field hedge and called to know how long she was to be with Rosy, she had all the rest still to milk, and why hadn't she even brought in a bucketful yet?

The maid hastened in and told her mistress, and master too, what she had seen.

'Ah! fax, I knowed,' said Dame Pendar to her husband, 'and didn't I always tell 'e something was the matter that Rosy wouldn't yield half her milk. And surely,' she continued to the milkmaid, 'thou must have a four-leaved-clover about thee; give me the wad in thy hat that I may look through it.'

She examined it, and sure enough found a stem of white clover, or three-leaved grass, with four leaves on it. The mistress asked how big the Small People were, and how dressed.

'But few of them are more than half a yard or so high,' the maid replied; 'the women not so tall, yet they looked beautiful, all dressed like gentry; the women wore gowns as gay as a flower-garden in summer; their flaxen hair fell in long curls on their necks; and the men were very smart, all like soldiers or huntsmen, so it seemed to me. But they made dreadful faces at you, and glared as if they would be the death of 'e. I shouldn't like to be in your shoes.'

'Our best cow is as bad as bewitched,' said Dame Pendar to her husband, 'and what shall we do to drive the plagues of sprites?'

Her husband told her not to be so greedy; for old folk said that the Small People always brought good luck when unmolested and their doings were not pried on by curious fools; for his part, he was content to leave well alone. She made no reply, but – determined to have her way, next morning, betimes, unknown to her good man – she trotted off to Penberth and consulted a red-haired woman that Mr Pendar could not abide, because she was reputed, and truly, to be a witch.

'I'll drive them from our best cow, and from Baranhual too, if it can be done,' said Dame Pendar to the hag. 'Nothing easier,' replied she, 'for they can't endure the sea, nor anything that comes therefrom,

and, above all, they abhor salt; so you only have to scatter it over
your cow and wash her udder in brine or sea water, and sprinkle it
about your place.'

Dame Pendar hastened home and, without delay, powdered Rosy
with salt, bathed her udder in brine and sprinkled it about the fields
and town-place.

In the evening, betimes, she went herself to milk her best cow, and
carried two buckets, thinking they would both be filled. Rosy,
without budging, let her be seated and milk a little; but, feeling her
udder thumped and roughly shaken when she withheld her flow, she
kicked the pail to shivers, laid Dame Pendar sprawling, then tossed
her greedy mistress heels over head, and galloped off, 'belving' like a
mad thing.

All the people in Baranhual could not stop her in a corner and, from
that day, not a drop of milk did they get from her. For days and nights

she would roam about the farm, followed by her heifer – no hedges stopped them – and both bellowing all the time like cows that had lost their calves. Before Christmas they became hair-pinched, lean and lousy; and all the other cattle on Baranhual were as bad.

Mr Pendar, being ignorant of what his wife had done, sought aid from, and brought to his farm, all the most noted conjurers, pellars and white witches in the West Country to arrest the run of bad luck that pursued everything belonging to him. They bled his diseased cattle on straw, burned the straw and blood, carried flaming torches of a night around the folds. Fire was also borne – with the sun's course – around sown fields. Bonfires were lit and his cattle forced through their flame. Other rites were performed according to old usages only known to pellars. Even his finest calf was burned alive. But all was of no avail.

To leave nothing undone, they cut down or rooted up all barberry bushes that grew about on orchard hedges and elsewhere; but Mr Pendar's crops were blighted all the same. In the meantime Rosy and her heifer were seldom seen, but often heard bellowing about Pednsawnack, over Porguarnon, or in other dangerous cleves and unfrequented places: they could not be brought into the town-place to undergo spells or counter-spells. But when more than a year had passed, and the next Buryan fair came round, Mr Pendar made up his mind to sell Rosy and her heifer. All Baranhual men and boys, with many neighbours mustered, and after much trouble drove them on to the churchtown road. But they could neither be got to fair nor home again. After following them on horseback till night, Mr Pendar caught a glimpse of Rosy and her heifer racing over Sennen Green towards Gwenvor Sands, and they were nevermore seen. Dame Pendar, from the time she was kicked and tossed, was rickety till the day of her death. The milkmaid, too, from a spanking damsel who had her choice of sweethearts, in less than a year became a dowdy that no young man cared for or would look at. From that time everything went wrong with the Pendars, and, in a few generations, those of the name who remained in Buryan had not an inch of land to call their own.

The Changeling

One afternoon in harvest time a hundred years or more ago, a woman called Jenny Trayer who lived in Brea Vean (a little out-of-the-way place at the foot of Chapel Carn Brea) gave her baby suck, rocked it to sleep, then covered up the fire, placed fire-hook and furze-prong across the hearth for good luck, and, leaving the child alone, away she hastened over to Brea to 'help cut the neck'. It was nearly dark when the last handful of wheat, called 'the neck', was tied up and cut by the reapers throwing their reap-hooks at it. Then it took a bit longer to cry the neck according to the old custom of the harvest-hands dividing themselves into three bands – one party calling, three times, as loud as they could cry, 'We have it, we have it, we have it!' The second demanding, 'What have ye? What have ye? What have ye?' And the third replying, 'A neck, a neck, a neck!' Then all join, hats in hands, in a 'Hip! hip! hip! Hurrah!'

Jenny, thinking about her babe all alone, did not stop for the neck-cutting carouse, but got a good drink of beer, and her neck-cake to take home; and hastened away. When she opened her door she saw by the moonlight that the cradle was overturned. Straw and rags were on the floor, but no child was in sight.

Jenny groped round the room a long time; then, not finding any live embers among the ashes, she took the tinder-box and struck a light. In searching all the holes and corners she came to the wood corner, and there among turves, ferns and furze she found the child fast asleep. Being very tired she took him up and went to bed. Next morning when she looked at the babe by daylight, it seemed to her that there was something strange about it – she didn't know what – it was hearty enow, for it seemed never satisfied unless it was all the time sucking or eating; it would roar like a bull if it did not have its will; and always wanted to be in her arms or eating pap.

The poor woman would not do her chores and had no rest in her life with the squalling, hungry brat. Yet with all its sucking and eating it seemed wasting to skin and bone. So it kept on all the winter – the more it ate the leaner it became. Many of the neighbours shook their heads when they saw it and said they feared the Small People had played her a trick that afternoon when she went to 'neck-cutting'. 'Whether or no,' said they, 'you can do nothing better, Jenny, than to bathe it in the Chapel Well as soon as May comes round.'

Accordingly the first Wednesday in May she took it on her back and trudged away to Chapel Uny Well. Three times she put it through the water from west to east, then dragged it three times round the well against the sun. Whether the bath made it any better or not she could not tell in one week. The following Wednesday, however, the troublesome creature seemed to expect the jaunt, and to enjoy it as he rode on her shoulder over hill and moor to the spring, where it had the same ducking again. The third Wednesday was a wet day; yet, not to spoil the spell, Jenny took the brat, placed it astride her shoulder, held one foot in her hand, while he grasped her hair to keep himself steady as they beat over the moors against wind and rain. The thing seemed to enjoy the storm and crowed like a cock when the wind roared the loudest.

They had nearly passed round Chapel Carn Brea and were coming by some large rocks near the open moor when she heard a shrill voice, seemingly above her head, call out–

'Tredrill! Tredrill!
Thy wife and children greet thee well.'

Jenny was surprised to hear the shrill voice and nobody in sight. When she stopped an instant to look round, the thing on her shoulder cried out in a voice as loud and shrill –

'What care I for wife and child,
When I ride on Dowdy's back to the Chapel Well,
And have got of pap my fill?'

Frightened out of her senses to hear the miserable little object talk like a man about his wife and his child, the poor woman cast it on the ground and there it lay sprawling, until she took courage, threw it across her shoulder, and ran back as fast as her feet would carry her till she came to Brea town. She stopped before some houses a little below Brea mansion, and threw down the thing that clung to her neck for dear life on to a dung-heap beside the road.

The women of Brea all ran out to see what could be the matter. As soon as she recovered her breath she told them what she had heard. 'Ah!' exclaimed one, 'didn't I tell thee, months ago, that thee wert nursing a small body's brat, ever since the neck-cutting night when

thy child was spirited away, and that thing left in his place.'

'Shure enow,' said another, 'anybody of common sense might see that. Only look at the thing there, sprawling upon his back in the mud. Did one ever see a Christian cheeld like that, with his goggle eyes squinting one way, his ugly mouth drawn another, and his pinched-up nose all a-wry too?'

'And now, Jenny,' broke in the oldest crone, ''tis lucky for 'e that I can tell 'e what you must do to get rid of this unlucky bucca and get back thy own dear cheeld. Now there's an old way, and I don't know but it es the best; and that es to put the small body upon the ashes and beat it well with a broom; then lay it naked under a church-way stile; there leave et, and keep out of sight and hearan till the turn of night; and, nine times out of ten, the thing will be took off and the stolen cheeld put in his place. There's another plan but I never seed it tried – to make by night a smoky fire, with green ferns and dry. When the chimney and house are full of smoke as one can bear, throw the changeling on the hearthstone, go out of the house, turn three times round; when one enters the right cheeld will be restored.'

The women of Brea – resolved to try what a beating on the ashes pile would do towards getting rid of the goblin – threw it on a heap near at hand and commenced belabouring it with their brooms. But they had scarcely touched it than it set up such a roar that it was heard in Brea mansion, and Dame Ellis came running down the town-place to see what could be the matter. She asked what they were beating in that cruel way. Being nearly dark and the wet ashes sticking to the creature she couldn't tell what gave out such a doleful noise.

'Why mistress,' says Jenny, 'that thing there on the ashes is what was left in our house when my poor child was spirited away by Small People, while I was reaping in your field the very day we cut the neck. All the neighbours know the trouble I've had ever since – how this thing that looked like my child have been all the time screeching, sucking or eating, and have never grown a bit, nor will make any use of his legs.'

Then she went on to tell how she had just been frightened out of her wits on the third journey to the Well, with the monster she carried speaking in words when before it only uttered animal-like noises.

Dame Ellis, lifting the creature from the ashes, said to Jenny, 'I believe that thou wert either drunk or in a waking-dream when passing round the hill and that this child, used so ill, is as truly thine as any thou hast born. Now take it home, wash it well, feed it regular, and don't thee leave it all day lying in its cradle; and, if thee canst not make it thrive, send for Dr Madron.'

Jenny and the other women at first refused to comply with Dame Ellis's advice; told her that she knew next to nothing about such matters, and related many things to prove that the creature was no mortal's child, till the lady tired of their stories and turned to go, saying to Jenny, 'My husband shall come out and talk to thee; peradventure he may convince thee of thy error.'

Squire Ellis and his wife being Quakers – a sect then but little known in the west – they were thought by Brea women, and many others, to be little better than unbelieving pagans, 'Who haven't the grace,' said they, 'to know anything about such creatures as spriggans, piskies, knackers (knockers of the mines) and other small folks, good or bad, that haunt our carns, moors, and mines; who can vanish or make themselves visible when and how they please, as all more enlightened folks know.'

They well knew, however, what concerned them more – that Squire Ellis was their landlord and that, quiet and Quaker-like as he and his wife were in their talk, and demure in their looks, they were not to be trifled with; and that their will was law for all living on their estate unless they could contrive to deceive them.

Squire Ellis came down and finding that Jenny (with her bantling and all the others) were gone into a house, where he heard them talking loudly, he had nothing to say to them; perhaps he kept an eye on the proceedings.

Determined to have their way, the Brea women waited until all was dark in the great house, then Jenny was sent out with her spriggan and another women who was very knowing about changelings. They passed quietly up Brea town-place and left the creature that had been such a plague to them asleep under a stile on the church-way path crossing a field from Brea lane.

Jenny returned to Brea Vean and there stayed till morning. Being fatigued and worried she overslept herself, for it was nearly daybreak when she awoke and hurried away, between hopes and fears, to the stile. There, sure enough, she found her own dear child sleeping on dry straw. The infant was as clean, from head to foot, as water could make it, and wrapped up in a piece of old gay-flowered chintz, which small folks often covet and steal from furze bushes, when it is placed there in the sun to dry.

Jenny nursed her recovered child with great care, but there was always something queer about it, as there always is with one that has been in the fairies' power – if only for a few days. It was constantly ailing and complaining, and, as soon as it was able to toddle, it would wander far away to all sorts of out-of-the-way places. The good lady of Brea often came to see it and brought it many nice things that its mother could not afford to buy, and when he was about nine years of age Squire Ellis took the changeling (as he was always called) into his service, but he was found to be such a poor innocent that he could never be trusted to work in fields alone, much less with cattle, as a whim would take him every now and then to leave his work and wander away over hills and moors for days together. Yet he was found useful for attending to rearing cattle and sheep – then kept in great numbers on the unenclosed grounds of Brea. He was so careful of his master's flock in lambing times that there was seldom any lost. Forsaken or weakly lambs were often given to him by the neighbours and he contrived to rear them so well that, in a few years, he had a good flock of his own that Squire Ellis and everyone else allowed him to pasture wherever he and his sheep chose to wander – everybody knew the poor changeling and made him welcome. When he grew to man's estate, however, he became subject to fits, and had to remain at home with his mother a great part of his time.

Yet, when the fits were over, nothing could restrain his propensity for wandering, and his sheep, goats and even calves always followed, and seemed equally to enjoy their rambles. He often talked to himself, and many believed that he was then holding converse with some of the fairy tribe, only visible to him, who enticed him to roam the carns, hills and moors – their usual haunts.

When about thirty years of age he was missed for several days; and his flock had been noticed, staying longer than usual near the same place, on a moor between the Chapel Hill and Bartinney, and there – surrounded by his sheep – he was found, lying on a quantity of rushes which he had pulled and collected for making sheep-spans.

He lay, with his arm under his head, apparently in sweet sleep, but the poor changeling of Brea was dead.